UNITS 7-12

INTER·ACTIVE
Mathematics
Activities & Investigations

GLENCOE
Macmillan/McGraw-Hill

New York, New York   Columbus, Ohio   Mission Hills, California   Peoria, Illinois

Send all inquiries to:
Glencoe Division, Macmillan/McGraw-Hill
936 Eastwind Drive
Westerville, OH 43081

ISBN: 0-02-824486-9 (Student Resource Book)

1 2 3 4 5 6 7 8 9 10 VH/LH-P 01 00 99 98 97 96 95 94

To the Student:

Here is a book that will make middle school mathematics interesting and valuable for you. It is not like most other books that you have used; it doesn't have pages and pages of problems. What it does have, though, are activities, projects, and investigations that will help you become a good problem-solver. You will learn new ideas that build on what you have learned already, and you will use these ideas in solving real-life problems. At times you will learn with others in pairs and in groups and this will help you later in life when most problems are solved together. We believe that this book will create both excitement and an understanding of mathematics.

Best wishes for a successful year.

Sincerely,

David Foster   *Sandie Gilliam*

Kay McClain   *Barney Martinez*

Jack Price   *Linda Dritsas*

AUTHORS INTERACTIVE MATHEMATICS

DAVID FOSTER

"The national goal is to develop mathematical power for all students. My vision for learning mathematics includes a student-oriented classroom culture, where students are taking charge of their own learning and are actively engaged in a curriculum that reflects today's world, not the mathematics of 150 years ago."

David Foster (signature)

Former Teaching Consultant
   Middle Grades Mathematics
   Renaissance
Morgan Hill, California
Author of Units 1, 2, 5, 6, 7, 8, 10, 11, 13, 15, 16, 17, and 18

David Foster received his B.A. in mathematics from San Diego State University and has taken graduate courses in computer science at San Jose State University. He has taught mathematics and computer science for nineteen years at the middle school, high school, and college level. Mr. Foster is a founding member of the California Mathematics Project Advisory Committee and was Co-Director of the Santa Clara Valley Mathematics Project. Most recently, he has taken the position of Consulting Author for Glencoe Publishing. Mr. Foster is a member of many professional organizations including the National Council of Teachers of Mathematics and regularly conducts in-service workshops for teachers. He is also the author of a book on computer science.

SANDIE GILLIAM

"Many students only see mathematics as isolated number facts and formulas to memorize. By using this program, which incorporates the mathematics into a context of large, real-life units tied together with literature, science, and history, the middle school student can find meaning in the mathematics."

Sandie Gilliam (signature)

Mathematics Teacher
San Lorenzo Valley High School
Felton, California
Co-author of Unit 14

Sandie Gilliam received her B.A. from San Jose State University and is a mentor teacher and instructor for the Monterey Bay Area Mathematics Project. She was a semi-finalist for the Presidential Award for Excellence in the Teaching of Mathematics in the state of California. Ms. Gilliam has served as a consultant for the California Department of Education and many local school districts and county offices of education. She is a member of the National Council of Teachers of Mathematics and is a frequent speaker at conferences and teacher in-service workshops. Ms. Gilliam was a writer and consultant for Glencoe's *Investigating Mathematics: An Interactive Approach.*

JACK PRICE

"This program is designed to help students become mathematically powerful as they develop problem-solving skills and self-reliance, as well as the ability to work well with others. At the same time, they will strengthen their basic skills and be exposed to new and exciting ideas in mathematics."

Jack Price (signature)

Co-Director, Center for Science
   and Mathematics Education
California State Polytechnic
   University
Pomona, California
Author of Unit 3

Jack Price received his B.A. from Eastern Michigan University and his Doctorate in Mathematics Education from Wayne State University. Dr. Price has been active in mathematics education for over 40 years, 38 of those years at grades K through 12. In his current position, he teaches mathematics and methods courses for preservice teachers and consults with school districts on curriculum change. He is president of the National Council of Teachers of Mathematics, is a frequent speaker at professional conferences, conducts many teacher in-service workshops, and is an author of numerous mathematics instructional materials.

INTERACTIVE MATHEMATICS AUTHORS

KAY McCLAIN

"Building conceptual understanding in mathematics challenges us to re-define what it means to know and do mathematics. This program was developed to allow teachers to become facilitators of learning while students explore and investigate mathematics — strengthening their understanding and stimulating interest."

Kay McClain

Doctoral Candidate
George Peabody College
Vanderbilt University
Nashville, Tennessee
Author of Unit 9, Co-author of Unit 14

BARNEY MARTINEZ

"Students learn mathematics best when their teacher enables them to become actively involved in worthwhile mathematical investigations. Students should be encouraged to interact with each other. Then, through their collaborative efforts, students build their own understanding of mathematics."

Barney Martinez

Mathematics Teacher
Jefferson High School
Daly City, California
Co-Author of Unit 12

LINDA DRITSAS

"This program is designed to encourage students to be creative and inventive, while gaining mathematical power. Open-ended situations and investigations provide the setting that allows students to work at varying depths, while nurturing their natural curiosity to learn."

Linda Dritsas

Mathematics Coordinator
Fresno Unified School District
Fresno, California
Author of Unit 4, Co-author of Unit 12

Kay McClain received her B.A. from Auburn University and her Educational Specialist degree from the University of Montevallo in Montevallo, Alabama. While a teacher at Mountain Brook Middle School in Birmingham, she received the Presidential Award for Excellence in the Teaching of Mathematics in the state of Alabama. Ms. McClain is a Woodrow Wilson fellow and a member of the National Council of Teachers of Mathematics. She regularly conducts teacher in-service workshops and is a frequent speaker at local, state, and national mathematics education conferences. She is also an author of middle school mathematics instructional materials.

Barney Martinez received his B.S. in mathematics from The University of San Francisco and is an instructor of pre-service mathematics teachers at the College of Notre Dame in Belmont, California. Mr. Martinez currently serves on the Mathematics Development Team of the California Department of Education and the Pursuing Excellence Revision Advisory Committee. He is a member of the National Council of Teachers of Mathematics and is very active as a speaker and workshop leader at professional development conferences.

Linda Dritsas received her B.A. and M.A. from California State University at Fresno. She taught middle school mathematics for many years and, for two years, taught mathematics at California State University at Fresno. Ms. Dritsas has been the Central Section President of the California Mathematics Council and is a member of the National Council of Teachers of Mathematics and the Association for Supervision and Curriculum Development. She frequently conducts mathematics teacher in-service workshops and is an author of numerous mathematics instructional materials, including those for middle school students and teachers.

CONTRIBUTORS INTERACTIVE MATHEMATICS

Each of the Consultants read all 18 units while each Reviewer read one unit. The Consultants and Reviewers gave suggestions for improving the Student Resource Books, Teacher's Editions, Cooperative Group Cards, Posters, and Transparencies. The Writers wrote the Student Diversity Strategies that appear in the Teacher's Edition.

CONSULTANTS

Dr. Judith Jacobs, *Units 1-18*
Director, Center for Science and Mathematics Education
California State Polytechnic University
Pomona, California

Dr. Cleo M. Meek, *Units 1-18*
Mathematics Consultant, Retired
North Carolina Dept. of Public Instruction
Raleigh, North Carolina

Beatrice Moore-Harris,
Units 1-18
College Board Equity 2000 Site Coordinator
Fort Worth Independent School District
Fort Worth, Texas

Deborah J. Murphy, *Units 1-18*
Mathematics Teacher
Killingsworth Jr. High School, ABC Unified School District
Cerritos, California

Javier Solorzano, *Units 1-18*
Mathematics Teacher
South El Monte High School
South El Monte, California

WRITERS

Student Diversity Teacher's Edition

Dr. Gilbert J. Cuevas
Professor of Mathematics Education
University of Miami
Coral Gables, Florida

Sally C. Mayberry, *Ed.D.*
Assistant Professor Mathematics/Science Education
St. Thomas University
Miami, Florida

REVIEWERS

John W. Anson, *Unit 11*
Mathematics Teacher
Arroyo Seco Junior High School
Valencia, California

Laura Beckwith, *Unit 13*
Mathematics Department Chairperson
William James Middle School
Fort Worth, Texas

Betsy C. Blume, *Unit 6*
Vice Principal/ Director of Curriculum
Valleyview Middle School
Denville, New Jersey

James F. Bohan, *Unit 11*
Mathematics K-12 Program Coordinator
Manheim Township School District
Lancaster, Pennsylvania

Dr. Carol Fry Bohlin, *Unit 14*
Director, San Joaquin Valley Mathematics Project
Associate Professor, Mathematics Education
California State University, Fresno
Fresno, California

David S. Bradley, *Unit 9*
Mathematics Teacher/Department Chairperson
Jefferson Jr. High
Kearns, Utah

Dr. Diane Briars, *Unit 9*
Mathematics Specialist
Pittsburgh City Schools
Pittsburgh, Pennsylvania

INTERACTIVE MATHEMATICS CONTRIBUTORS

Jackie Britton, *Unit 18*
Mathematics Teacher
V. W. Miller Intermediate
Pasadena, Texas

Sybil Y. Brown, *Unit 8*
Mathematics Teacher
Franklin Alternative Middle
School
Columbus, Ohio

Blanche Smith Brownley, *Unit 18*
Supervising Director of
Mathematics (Acting)
District of Columbia Public
Schools
Washington, D.C.

Bruce A. Camblin, *Unit 7*
Mathematics Teacher
Weld School District 6
Greeley, Colorado

Cleo Campbell, *Unit 15*
Coordinator of Mathematics,
K-12
Anne Arundel County
Public Schools
Annapolis, Maryland

Savas Carabases, *Unit 13*
Mathematics Supervisor
Camden City School District
Camden City, New Jersey

W. Karla Castello, *Unit 6*
Mathematics Teacher
Yerba Buena High School
San Jose, California

Diane M. Chase, *Unit 16*
Mathematics Teacher/
Department Chairperson
Pacific Jr. High School
Vancouver, Washington

Dr. Phyllis Zweig Chinn, *Unit 9*
Professor of Mathematics
Humboldt State University
Arcata, California

Nancy W. Crowther, *Unit 17*
Mathematics Teacher
Sandy Springs Middle School
Atlanta, Georgia

Regina F. Cullen, *Unit 13*
Supervisor of Mathematics
West Essex Regional Schools
North Caldwell, New Jersey

Sara J. Danielson, *Unit 17*
Mathematics Teacher
Albany Middle School
Albany, California

Lorna Denman, *Unit 10*
Mathematics Teacher
Sunny Brae Middle School
Arcata, California

Richard F. Dube, *Unit 4*
Mathematics Supervisor
Taunton High School
Taunton, Massachusetts

Mary J. Dubsky, *Unit 1*
Mathematics Curriculum
Specialist
Baltimore City Public Schools
Baltimore, Maryland

Dr. Leo Edwards, *Unit 5*
Director, Mathematics/
Science Education Center
Fayetteville State University
Fayetteville, North Carolina

Connie Fairbanks, *Unit 7*
Mathematics Teacher
South Whittier Intermediate
School
Whittier, California

Ana Marina C. Gomezgil, *Unit 15*
District Translator/Interpreter
Sweetwater Union
High School District
Chula Vista, California

Sandy R. Guerra, *Unit 9*
Mathematics Teacher
Harry H. Rogers Middle
School
San Antonio, Texas

Rick Hall, *Unit 4*
Curriculum Coordinator
San Bernardino County
Superintendent of Schools
San Bernardino, California

Carolyn Hansen, *Unit 14*
Instructional Specialist
Williamsville Central Schools
Williamsville, New York

Jenny Hembree, *Unit 8*
Mathematics Teacher
Shelby Co. East Middle
School
Shelbyville, Kentucky

Susan Hertz, *Unit 16*
Mathematics Teacher
Paul Revere Middle School
Houston, Texas

Janet L. Hollister, *Unit 5*
Mathematics Teacher
LaCumbre Middle School
Santa Barbara, California

Dorothy Nachtigall Hren, *Unit 12*
Mathematics Teacher/
Department Chairperson
Northside Middle School
Norfolk, Virginia

Grace Hutchings, *Unit 3*
Mathematics Teacher
Parkman Middle School
Woodland Hills, California

Lyle D. Jensen, *Unit 18*
Mathematics Teacher
Albright Middle School
Villa Park, Illinois

Robert R. Jones, *Unit 7*
Chief Consultant,
Mathematics, Retired
North Carolina Department
of Public Instruction
Raleigh, North Carolina

Mary Kay Karl, *Unit 3*
Mathematics Coordinator
Community Consolidated
School District 54
Schaumburg, Illinois

Janet King, *Unit 14*
Mathematics Teacher
North Gulfport Junior High
Gulfport, Mississippi

Franca Koeller, *Unit 17*
Mathematics Mentor Teacher
Arroyo Seco Junior High
School
Valencia, California

Louis La Mastro, *Unit 2*
Mathematics/Computer
Science Teacher
North Bergen High School
North Bergen, New Jersey

Patrick Lamberti, *Unit 6*
Supervisor of Mathematics
Toms River Schools
Toms River, New Jersey

Dr. Betty Larkin, *Unit 14*
Mathematics Coordinator
K - 12
Lee County School District
Fort Myers, Florida

Ann Lawrence, *Unit 1*
Mathematics
Teacher/Department
Coordinator
Mountain Brook Jr. High
School
Mountain Brook, Alabama

Catherine Louise Marascalco,
Unit 3
Mathematics Teacher
Southaven Elementary
School
Southaven, Mississippi

Dr. Hannah Masterson, *Unit 10*
Mathematics Specialist
Suffolk Board of
Cooperative Education
Dix Hills, New York

Betty Monroe Nelson, *Unit 8*
Mathematics Teacher
Blackburn Middle School
Jackson, Mississippi

Dale R. Oliver, *Unit 2*
Assistant Professor of
Mathematics
Humboldt State University
Arcata, California

Carol A. Pudlin, *Unit 4*
Mathematics Teacher/
Consultant
Griffiths Middle School
Downey, California

Diane Duggento Sawyer,
Unit 15
Mathematics Chairperson
Exeter Area Junior High
Exeter, New Hampshire

Donald W. Scheuer, Jr., *Unit 12*
Mathematics Department
Chairperson
Abington Junior High
Abington, Pennsylvania

Linda S. Shippey, *Unit 8*
Mathematics Teacher
Bondy Intermediate School
Pasadena, Texas

Barbara Smith, *Unit 1*
Mathematics Supervisor,
K-12
Unionville-Chadds Ford
School District
Kennett Square, Pennsylvania

Stephanie Z. Smith, *Unit 14*
Project Assistant
University of Wisconsin-
Madison
Madison, Wisconsin

Dora M. Swart, *Unit 11*
Mathematics Teacher
W. F. West High School
Chehalis, Washington

Ciro J. Tacinelli, Sr., *Unit 8*
Curriculum Director:
Mathematics
Hamden Public Schools
Hamden, Connecticut

Kathy L. Terwelp, *Unit 12*
K-8 Mathematics Supervisor
Summit Public Schools
Summit, New Jersey

Marty Terzieff, *Unit 18*
Secondary Math Curriculum
Chairperson
Mead Junior High School
Mead, Washington

Linda L. Walker, *Unit 18*
Mathematics Teacher
Cobb Middle School
Tallahassee, Florida

C O N T E N T S

UNIT
7

TAKE IT FROM THE TOP
BUILDING MATH POWER

Interdisciplinary Applications

Teens In the News

Have you ever asked yourself this question:

When am I ever going to use this stuff?

Each unit begins with a *Teens in the News* feature about a successful, highly motivated teen who uses mathematics as an aid to his or her success.

UNIT 7 **Dennis Daughters** of Castro Valley, California, opened Denny's Please Touch Store, a toy store for the visually handicapped, when he was 9 years old.

UNIT 8 **Mary Rodas** of New York, New York, has served as an advisor to CATCO Toys, Inc., since she was 14 and is now the Vice President of Marketing.

UNIT 9 **David Eilers** of Roswell, Georgia, started David's Mowing Service which grew into a $49,000 business by the time he was 15.

UNIT 10 **Tiger Woods** of Cypress, California, is a teen who has been named amateur golfer of the year by national golfing publications.

UNIT 11 **Susan Behm** of Westminster, Colorado, is a teen who operates Suzie Q's Embroidery, which specializes in computerized embroidery on clothing.

UNIT 12 **Laurie Moran** of Bangor, Maine, spent part of her summer vacations sailing along the Atlantic coast and learning about navigation.

Team Projects

The *Team Project* in each unit places you in a problem-solving situation that may have confronted the actual teen in *Teens in the News*.

UNIT 7 **Magic Touch** Your team will learn about the braille system and put it to work in forming magic squares.

UNIT 8 **Why Buy?** Your team will survey students to discover how they spend their money.

UNIT 9 **Four Seasons** Your team will brainstorm to help turn "Green Seasons" into a year-round business.

UNIT 10 **Your Best Shot** Your team will research to discover the odds of getting a hole in one.

UNIT 11 **Designs in Time** Your team will create an original design and "program" a computer to make the design.

UNIT 12 **Nautical Jargon** Your team of "sailors" will search out the special words and terms used in sailing.

CONTENTS

UNIT 8

DATA Sense
STATISTICS AND DATA ANALYSIS

Interdisciplinary Applications

What's Different About INTERACTIVE MATHEMATICS?

What's a *toolkit*? What's a *menu station*? What is *assessment*? What's the purpose of a *journal* and a *portfolio*? You may not be very familiar with some of these terms. The following explanations may be helpful to you since nearly every unit contains these terms.

Mathematics Toolkit Your math hosts are the characters in a script in which new mathematics tools are presented and explained. You are encouraged to use these tools to help solve problems and to add your own tools that you discover.

MENU station A

Menu Station Activity Each Menu Station Activity is broken into five or six stations. In some Menu Station Activities, your group chooses which menu station activity to complete. In others, your group moves around the room and completes each station.

Assessment According to the dictionary, assessment is the act of determining importance, size, or value. In school, assessment usually refers to the process of assigning grades. Here are some of the ways that assessment is continually built into your Student Resource Book.

- •Pre-Assessment Activity
- •Group Investigation
- •Individual Investigation
- •Final Assessment Activity

JOURNAL PROMPT

- •Journals Journals are a perfect way to connect mathematics with your writing. In your journal, you are encouraged to summarize key topics, as well as to write about your accomplishments and frustrations.

PORTFOLIO SUGGESTION

- •Portfolios A portfolio is a collection of your work that you keep in a folder or bind in book form. A portfolio includes work that you have created and selected. In some cases, you will select what you think is your best work. In other cases, your teacher will select the work to be included.

CONTENTS

UNIT 9

DON'T FENCE ME IN

AREA AND PERIMETER

Interdisciplinary Applications

Computer Investigations

Can you imagine what your life would be like without technology? It's truly difficult to imagine a world without computers, CDs, VCRs, calculators, and all the other wonderful electronic gadgets. The Computer Investigations in your Student Resource Book will expose you to powerful applications, many of which you will be able to use for a lifetime. The Computer Investigation Software makes it easy to complete each activity.

Unit 8 Group Investigation   Homerun Consultants
A **spreadsheet** is used to help analyze the performance of several baseball players.

Unit 9 Activity Four   Home on the Range
A **spreadsheet** is used to investigate the impact of change in dimensions upon area.

Unit 10 Activity Seven   Chances Are...
A **BASIC** program is used to run simulations of games to determine if they are fair or unfair.

Unit 11 Activity Six   Spirolaterals
A **LOGO** program is used to explore spirolaterals and their properties.

Unit 12 Activity Five   The Pathfinders
A **LOGO** program is used to investigate paths and draw polygons.

CONTENTS

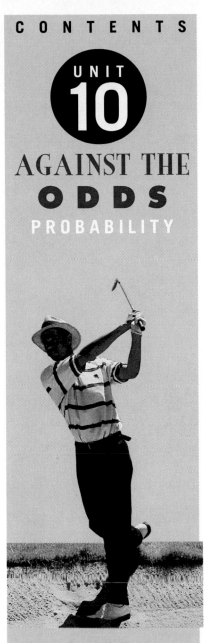

UNIT

10

AGAINST THE
O D D S
PROBABILITY

Interdisciplinary Applications

CONTENTS

UNIT 11

CYCLES
ALGEBRA PATTERNS

CONTENTS

UNIT 12

TREASURE ISLAND GEOMETRY AND MEASUREMENT

Interdisciplinary Applications

What's in the Back of Your Student Resource Book?

Have you ever wondered why all that extra material is in the back of textbooks? Have you ever used any of that stuff? In this book, the following items will be very useful to you as you work through all the activities and investigations.

PROBLEMS OF THE WEEK/EXTENDED PROBLEMS

At the end of each unit, you will find seven challenging Problems of the Week or Extended Problems connected to the mathematics of the unit. For example, the Problems of the Week and Extended Problems for Unit 8 are found on pages 66–72. These problems give you additional opportunities to explore the topics presented in the unit.

DATA BANK

This section, found on pages 235–260, is a group of references and resources designed to help you complete the activities and investigations or to complete an extension of an activity. One way you can think of the Data Bank is as a mini-reference library.

GLOSSARY/INDEX

The Glossary/Index, found on pages 261–272 contains an alphabetical listing of important words and terms. For some of the key words that you may not be familiar with, a definition is also given.

Take It From THE TOP

Looking Ahead

In this unit, you will see how mathematics can be used to discover new methods of learning. You will experience:

▶ using manipulatives to learn new concepts

▶ working cooperatively to solve problems

▶ explaining how you solve problems through writing, speaking, and modeling

▶ learning new ways of showing others what you have learned

▶ using technological tools such as calculators

Did You Ever Wonder?

What do mathematics and operating a store for the blind have to do with each other? Turn the page and see how Denny Daughters of Castro Valley, California, combined the two.

Teens in the News

Featuring: Dennis (Denny) F. Daughters
Age: 19
Hometown: Castro Valley, California
Career Goal: Broadcasting
Interests: Music and
        Disc Jockeying

Did you ever notice how all the great stuff in toy stores is packed in sealed boxes? It's really hard to know if you'll like the item when you only see the picture of it on the box. It's even harder for blind people like Denny Daughters.

Denny wanted there to be a store where blind kids could "see" and touch toys before buying them. So, when Denny was 9 years old, he opened **Denny's Please Touch Store.** All the toys in his store were out of their boxes for kids to "see" and touch.

Denny's Please Touch Store had gifts and toys for blind children. He had Monopoly®, Scrabble®, and checkers in braille. He even labeled the names of candy bars in braille!

Denny set up the displays in his store. He learned coin values by touch, folded bills a certain way to tell them apart, and used a talking calculator to help him figure expenses, compute taxes, and pay bills. He balanced his checkbook and took care of his employee's time cards.

More recently, Denny has been taking piano lessons and writing music. He's also a DJ for parties and weddings. Denny attends a junior college where he is majoring in broadcasting. The only thing Denny doesn't "see" is any limit to what he can do!

Can You Read This Music?

CLUES

1. Pitch names are written in the four upper dots of the braille cells.

    C   D   E   F   G   A   B

2. ⠛ is the sign for the fourth octave, where Middle C occurs. ⠸ is the sign for the third octave, which includes the seven notes below Middle C.

3. Rhythmic values are written in the lower dots of the braille cells.

    = ♩   = ♪

4. Bar lines are indicated by spaces in lines of braille.

Team Project

Magic Touch

The braille system of printing and writing was developed by Louis Braille in the early 1800s. Louis Braille was blinded in an accident in 1812 at the age of three.

Find out about the braille system. Write a paragraph, in braille, describing how this system was developed. Use the numbers 11 through 19 to form a magic square in braille. You can find the braille alphabet and numerals 0-9 in your Data Bank.

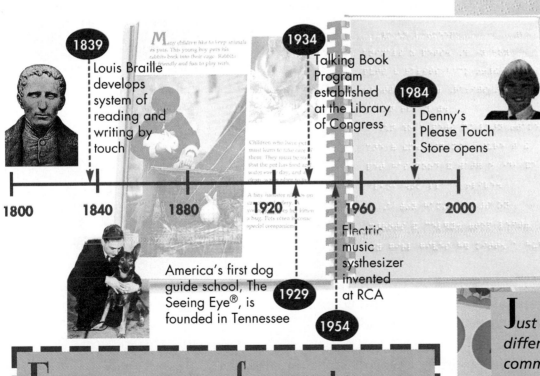

1839
Louis Braille develops system of reading and writing by touch

1934
Talking Book Program established at the Library of Congress

1984
Denny's Please Touch Store opens

1800   1840   1880   **1920**   1960   2000

1929
America's first dog guide school, The Seeing Eye®, is founded in Tennessee

1954
Electric music systhesizer invented at RCA

Just as Denny uses a different method of communication, you can learn different methods of communicating by completing the activities in this unit.

For more information

If you would like more information about reading materials for the blind, contact:

RECORDING FOR THE BLIND
20 Roszel Road
Princeton, New Jersey 08540

Setting the Scene

TEAM BUILDERS

Quad Squad

In this activity, you will encounter geometry in motion.

1. Get into squads of four or five students each. Select one member to be the safety coordinator. Everyone else should be blindfolded.

2. Each blindfolded member of the squad should grasp the rope with both hands. If there are only three blindfolded members, the safety coordinator should also grasp the rope. The safety coordinator should make sure all the members are spread out along the rope, but the actual distance between them does not matter.

3. The safety coordinator calls out the name of a quadrilateral (parallelogram, square, rectangle, rhombus, or trapezoid). The squad attempts to manipulate the rope into the shape of that quadrilateral according to the following rules.

   - Only blindfolded members of the squad may speak to each other.

   - Blindfolded members of the squad may move along the rope in any direction they wish. However, no one may remove the blindfold, let go of the rope, or exchange places along the rope.

4. When all the blindfolded members of the squad agree that the quadrilateral has been made, they may remove the blindfolds.

All members of the squad should discuss ways to improve the process at this time. Then a new safety coordinator should be selected and the squad should repeat the activity with a different quadrilateral.

As a group, prepare a report on how your squad worked on this activity. Consider the questions below in writing your report. Use them to get started, but don't write only an answer to each question or be limited to just these questions.

- Was your squad able to form the shape of each quadrilateral?
- What strategies did you find useful? Were there any that you started out using and then decided to reject?
- How did your squad arrive at a plan after the first try?

Hop, Skip, Jump

Place the seven game pieces, or bases, on the floor as shown below. Allow about 2 feet of space between each base. You will need to form two teams of three players. Each player for the Red Team should stand looking down at a ☞ sign and each player for the Blue Team should stand looking down at a ☜ sign. All players should be standing on the same side of the bases.

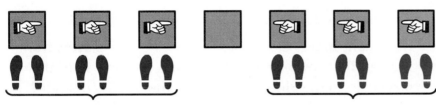

Red Team   Blue Team

The object of this game is for the members of the Red Team to make a series of moves to the right while the members of the Blue Team are making a series of moves to the left until all the members of each team end up on the opposite team's side. To play this game, you will need to keep in mind the following rules.

- All players must remain on one of the seven bases.
- The members of the Red Team may only move to the right.
- The members of the Blue Team may only move to the left.
- A player can move to a new base only if it is open. No two players can share a base.
- Players cannot switch bases simultaneously.

- You may pass only one player at a time and it must be according to the following restrictions.
- The player you pass must be from the other team (you may not pass players from your own team).
- The player you pass must be directly next to you (that is, there are no empty bases between you and the player).
- You can only pass if there is an open base directly on the other side of that player.

Play the game and keep a record of each move that is made. Then answer the following questions.

- How did you decide which team would move first?
- How many moves did it take to get all of the players from the Red Team over to the Blue Team's side and all of the players from the Blue Team over to the Red Team's side?
- What would be the least number of moves necessary?
- How do you know that you have the least number of moves possible?

Design a recording sheet to keep track of your strategies and your findings. Be sure that it is clear and complete.

Write a paragraph detailing your findings. Then answer the following questions.

- What would happen if there were more bases on each side of the blank base?
- What if there was a different number of bases on each side, like four on one side and five on the other side? Does your solution still work?

A Nutty Excursion

Jack and Jill went up the hill to visit Cordona's Concession Supply Company. They wanted to purchase 8 pounds of unsalted, roasted peanuts to use at the homecoming dance. When they arrived, Mrs. Cordona had only 6-pound and 10-pound measuring containers.

A few minutes later they left with 8 pounds of peanuts. How did they measure out exactly 8 pounds of peanuts? Is there more than one way they could have accomplished it? Make sure that your solution is complete.

Which of the amounts below can Jack and Jill measure?

1 pound	2 pounds	3 pounds	4 pounds	5 pounds
7 pounds	9 pounds	11 pounds	12 pounds	13 pounds

Write a report explaining your conclusions. Use any diagrams or charts you feel are necessary.

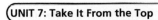

Pentomino + 1 = Hexomino

Y ou will be working with hexominoes in this activity. These are arrangements of six squares. In the arrangements, all squares must share at least one side with another square, and the vertices of the squares must coincide. Arrangement A below is allowed, while B is not.

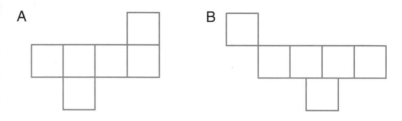

1. Make all of the possible *different* arrangements of six tiles. Record these by drawing them on centimeter grid paper. "Different" means an arrangement that can't be made from another arrangement by just turning or flipping it.
2. Of the arrangements you found above, circle the ones that can be folded into a box with a lid.

Write a one-page narrative on how your group worked on this activity. Consider the questions below in writing your narrative. Use them to get started, but don't write only an answer to each question or be limited to just these questions.

- How many different hexominoes were you able to form?
- What strategy did you use to find all the hexominoes, without repeating any of them?
- Did you make any discoveries or encounter any surprises from this activity? Explain.

TANGRAMS

The menu stations at which you will be working involve manipulating pieces of a puzzle called a tangram. The tangram is one of the world's oldest manipulatives. A tangram consists of seven simple closed shapes whose sides are line segments. In mathematics, these shapes are called **polygons.** When two segments of a polygon meet, they form an **angle.** The point where they meet is called the **vertex** of the angle.

A tangram contains five triangles, one parallelogram, and one square. A **triangle** is a polygon with three sides. As you learned in the Quad Squad activity, a **parallelogram** is a polygon with four sides (called a **quadrilateral**) that has both pairs of opposite sides parallel. A **square** is a quadrilateral with all sides congruent and all angles congruent.

Congruent sides are sides that have the same length. **Congruent angles** are angles that have the same measure.

To learn more about tangrams, refer to "A Story of the Tangram" in your Data Bank.

FREE THE TRAPEZOID

KEEP US TOGETHER

DOWN WITH CIRCLES

TANGRAM IS A SQUARE

FREE THE TRAPEZOID

MENU station A

My Shape's Bigger Than Yours!

Use the Tangram Polygons sheet (Blackline Master 7-2B) with this station.

1 **I**s the rectangle at the top larger than the square below it? Find out which figure is larger by covering each of them with tangram pieces.

2 **U**sing the tangram pieces, can you cover the square with:

- 2 pieces? • 3 pieces?
- 4 pieces? • 5 pieces?
- 6 pieces? • 7 pieces?

3 **U**sing tangram pieces, can you make a rectangle with:

- 2 pieces? • 3 pieces?
- 4 pieces? • 5 pieces?
- 6 pieces? • 7 pieces?

4 **W**rite a summary statement about any conclusions you made during this activity.

I Saw Cell Ease Please

Use the Tangram Polygons sheet (Blackline Master 7-2B) with this station.

1 An **isosceles triangle** has at least two congruent sides. A tangram has three different-sized triangles. Trace each of the three different triangles.

2 Can you cover the largest triangle with:
- 2 tangram pieces?
- 3 pieces?
- 4 pieces?
- 5 pieces?

3 How can you use tangram pieces to prove that the triangles you traced are isosceles triangles?

4 Each angle of a square is a **right angle**. Its measure is 90°. How does the angle formed by the two congruent sides of the triangles you traced compare to an angle of the square tangram piece?

5 Write a summary statement about any conclusions you made during this activity.

MENU
station
C

A PAIR OF YELLOW GRAHAMS?

Use the Tangram Polygons sheet (Blackline Master 7-2B) with this station.

1 Cover the parallelogram that is to the left of the square using exactly three tangram pieces. Can you do it three different ways?

2 How can you use your triangle tangram pieces to show that the opposite angles of the parallelogram are congruent?

3 Show that there are two parallelograms in a set of tangram pieces.

4 Write a summary statement about any conclusions you made during this activity.

Trap A What?

Use the Tangram Polygons sheet (Blackline Master 7-2B) with this station.

1 **A trapezoid** is a quadrilateral that has exactly one pair of parallel sides. The parallel sides of a trapezoid are called its **bases**. The **height** of a trapezoid is the shortest distance between its bases.

2 **U**sing the tangram pieces, can you cover the trapezoid on the Tangram Polygons sheet with:

- 2 pieces?
- 3 pieces?
- 4 pieces?
- 5 pieces?
- 6 pieces?
- 7 pieces?

3 **W**rite a summary statement about any conclusions you made during this activity.

MENU
station
E

Don't Con Me!

Polygons can be classified according to their common characteristics. Polygons with more than three sides can be classified as concave or convex.

1 **T**he polygons shown below are **convex** polygons. The dashed lines in the polygons are called **diagonals.** Using all seven tangram pieces, form a **concave** polygon— a polygon that is *not* convex.

2 **H**ow can you use tangram pieces to describe the difference between a convex polygon and a concave polygon?

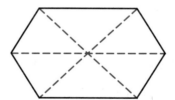
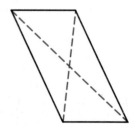

3 **A** polygon's name also describes it. Use a set of tangram pieces and the meaning of each prefix to form each polygon. Then label your polygons as concave or convex.

- penta- 5 • hexa-   6
- octa-   8 • nona-   9
- deca- 10 • dodeca- 12

4 **W**rite a summary statement about any conclusions you made during this activity. Include drawings of the polygons you created.

Clueless in Seattle

The information your group needs to know to solve a problem has been put on clue cards. Each member of your group will have a different piece of information, so your entire group will have to cooperate to solve the problem.

Each group will receive an envelope with six clue cards in it. There will be enough cards so that each member of your group will receive at least one. When the cards are distributed, you may look only at your own card. You may tell others what your evidence is, but you may not show your card to anyone else.

Your task is to work together to solve a problem. After you have solved the problem, write a one-page report that includes answers to the following questions.

- What strategies worked well in your group?

- How did the members of your group decide on a process for solving the problem?

- Was there more than one correct solution to the problem? Why or why not?

Fruit for Thought

Each type of fruit represents a single digit (0 - 9). Using what you know about the number system, determine the value of each fruit.

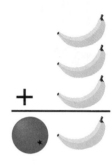

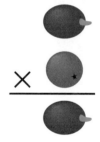

That's Sum Triangle!

Study the figure below carefully. How can the ten numbers in the small triangles be rearranged so that the sum of the four numbers in each of the three larger triangles is 46?

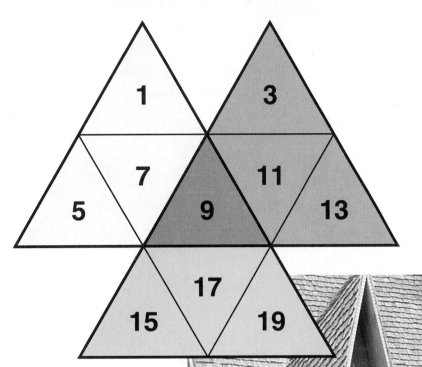

What discoveries or observations did you make as you solved this problem?

If the sum of the four numbers in each of the three larger triangles had to be a number other than 46, would you be able to solve the problem? Explain why or why not.

A Square with Round Corners

On a piece of plain paper, trace a counter nine times. Cut out the circles. Using the rational numbers listed below, write a different rational number on each piece.

With your group, place the counters in the circles of the square design so that the product of every three connected circles is $\frac{5}{16}$.

NUMBERS TO BE USED: $\frac{5}{6}$, $1\frac{1}{8}$, $\frac{1}{2}$, $\frac{3}{10}$, $\frac{3}{4}$, $\frac{1}{2}$, $1\frac{1}{4}$, $\frac{1}{3}$, $1\frac{7}{8}$

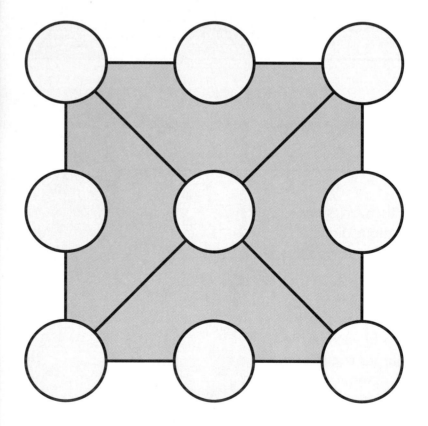

Save My Place

Cut nine index cards in half. Make two sets of cards containing the digits 1-9, one digit per card. On a large sheet of paper, make a copy of the figure shown below. Make sure that the digit cards will fit in the boxes.

Arrange the eighteen digit cards in the boxes to show the quotients of the expressions below.

58 ÷ 8	195.26 ÷ 6.5
0.156 ÷ 52	307.5 ÷ 15
64 ÷ 80	758.99 ÷ 7.1
0.343 ÷ 7	232.98 ÷ 33
575.64 ÷ 53.3	

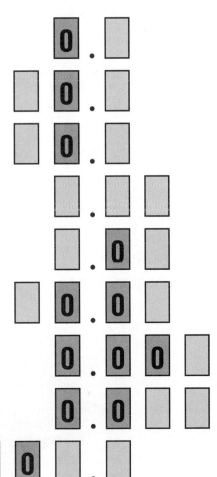

Finders Keepers

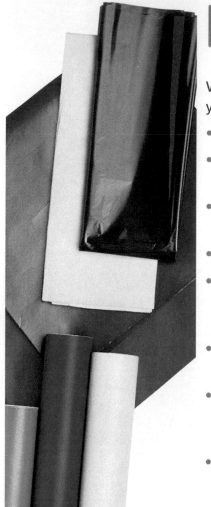

With a partner, see how many of the items in the following list you can find.

- A cylinder that has a height of about 100 millimeters.

- A rectangular object that has an area of about 96 square inches.

- A circular object that has a circumference of about 5 inches.

- Something that is 60 centimeters long.

- Someone's footprint that has an area of about 160 square centimeters. Use centimeter grid paper to explain how you know you have the "right" foot.

- The length, width and height of a rectangular solid—to the nearest centimeter.

- The length, width, and height of a large rectangular solid such as the teacher's desk, a filing cabinet, or the classroom itself, in centimeters and inches.

- The length, width, and height of a large rectangular solid such as the teacher's desk, a filing cabinet, or the classroom itself, in two nonstandard units of measure that you create. In other words, the units of measure are not found on a ruler.

- Two objects that could be covered with about the same amount of gift wrapping paper. Explain how you know you are correct.

- Two different-shaped containers that may hold about the same amount of water.

To Spin or Not to Spin

You will use the recording sheet that your teacher has provided to complete this activity.

Examine the three spinners on the recording sheet. Predict the results of spinning the top spinner 60 times. Record your predictions on the recording sheet. Place the closed end of a bobby pin over the center of the spinner. Place a pencil or the metal end of a compass in the center of the top spinner. Then spin the bobby pin 60 times and record your results. Explain your findings completely.

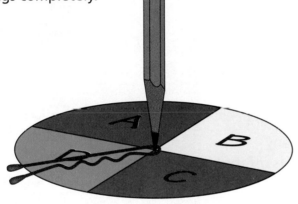

Predict the result of spinning the middle spinner 60 times. Record your predictions on the recording sheet. Using the procedure you used for the top spinner, spin the bobby pin on the middle spinner 60 times and record your results. Using the data you recorded, how would you describe the chances of spinning a 3? Explain.

Suppose you spin the middle spinner and the bottom spinner, and find the sum of the numbers. What are the possible sums? What is your prediction about the probability of each sum occurring in 80 spins? Record your prediction on the recording sheet. Then, spin each of the two spinners 80 times and record the sums. Study the results and make a drawing or graph of the results. Combine results with another pair of students and re-evaluate the outcomes. Explain your findings completely.

It Takes Two

You will use the diagram your teacher provides to solve this puzzle. Place a counter on each of the shaded boxes.

The goal of this activity is to keep an even number of counters in each row and in each column. To solve this puzzle, you will need to keep in mind the following rules.

- You can move exactly two counters.

- No more than four counters can be in any row or any column.

- You may not move any counters off the board.

- No two counters may occupy the same space at the same time.

- You cannot switch the position of one counter with the position of another counter on the same turn.

Work with a partner. Is there more than one solution? Explain why or why not.

Can the puzzle be solved if the diagonals also have to contain an even number of counters? Explain why or why not.

Can the puzzle be solved if three counters can be moved? if four counters are moved? Write a one-page report detailing your findings.

Apple Sacks

The apple sacks below have been labeled incorrectly.

- Your favorite apples, yellow delicious, are in one bag.

- Your least favorite apples, red delicious, are in another bag.

- The third bag contains an equal number of both red and yellow delicious apples.

The bags are labeled Y, R, and Y&R, but remember, the labels are incorrect. You want to find the bag of yellow delicious apples because they are your favorite.

You are allowed to pick one apple at a time from a bag. How many picks would you have to make to find out which bag is the bag with all yellow delicious apples? Be sure you can justify your conclusion. Use models, if necessary, to clarify your explanation.

Get the Hint?

Copy each of the names, locations, and types of shirts shown below, onto an index card, one item per card. For each category, shuffle the cards and then remove one card. Without looking at what's written on them, place these three cards inside an envelope with your group's name on it and give the envelope to your teacher. Shuffle all the remaining cards together and distribute an equal number of cards to each member of your group.

You will use your cards and the answers other group members give to determine what the cover of the next Threads catalog will look like. The three cards that are in the envelope you gave to the teacher tell what will be on the cover, so the cards that remain with your group tell what won't be.

One player asks the player to his or her left a question in this form: "Is (model's name) on the (location) wearing the (shirt type)? If the player being asked has a card that will eliminate one of these possibilities, he or she must show it to the player who asked the question. Continue in the same way, taking turns asking questions to confirm or eliminate possibilities. If you think you know the cover design, you may guess and look at the cards in the envelope. If you are wrong you may not guess again, but you may continue to be asked questions by the other players.

Models	Locations	Shirts
Alejandra	stairs	sweatshirt
Jenny	beach	short-sleeve T-shirt
Hector	deck	rugby shirt
Terrence	boat	sweater
Chris	campfire	hooded sweatshirt

Selection and Reflection

- Describe one thing you learned from working in a cooperative group in this unit.

- Describe one thing you learned by working with manipulatives in this unit.

- What was your favorite activity in this unit? Gather together the papers of the work you did in your favorite activity. Explain what the activity was about and why you liked it.

- Was there anything you studied in this unit that you still feel you don't understand? What do you think could be done to help you gain a better understanding?

Square Paths

The Problem

Beginning at the center S and moving only up, down, left, or right, how many different paths can you find to spell the word SQUARES?

```
                        S
                      S E S
                    S E R E S
                  S E R A R E S
                S E R A U A R E S
              S E R A U Q U A R E S
            S E R A U Q S Q U A R E S
              S E R A U Q U A R E S
                S E R A U A R E S
                  S E R A R E S
                    S E R E S
                      S E S
                        S
```

The Problem

The "supernova" star shown below is made up of 24 different pieces. Copy the figure and cut out the pieces. Reassemble the 24 pieces so that they form three smaller stars of the same shape. Each of the smaller stars will be the same shape as the original supernova.

The Problem

A word game uses cubes with letters on each face. In the figure below, every cube is exactly alike. Copy the representation of the faces of a cube below and fill in the letters as they are arranged on the letter cubes.

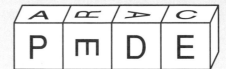

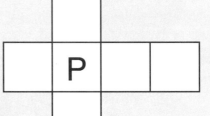

The Problem

Find the numbers for the boxes that add up to the numbers in the circles between them.

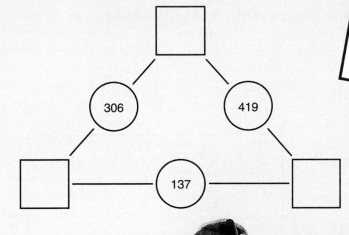

Boxing Match 2

Extension How is the sum of the numbers on a side of the triangle related to the number in the circle on that side?

A Square Deal

The Problem

If the length of a side of a square is s units, then the area of the square is A = s x s square units. In the diagram below, the area of square H is 64 square units and the area of square F is 49 square units. Find the areas of the other seven squares.

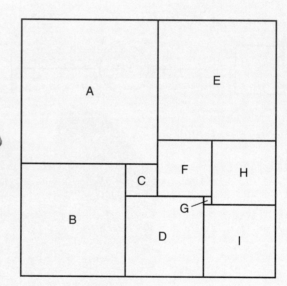

Extension What is the area of the entire figure?

The Problem

Contestants on The Wheel of Fortune usually ask for the letters R, S, T, N, and E when they start to solve a puzzle. That's because these are the four consonants and the vowel that occur most often in English words. The table below shows the average number of times that each letter occurs in a sample of 100 words.

Letter	Frequency	Letter	Frequency
A	8.2	N	7.0
B	1.4	O	8.0
C	2.8	P	2.0
D	3.8	Q	0.1
E	13.0	R	6.8
F	3.0	S	6.0
G	2.0	T	10.5
H	5.4	U	2.5
I	6.5	V	0.9
J	0.1	W	1.5
K	0.4	X	0.2
L	3.4	Y	2.0
M	2.5	Z	0.07

The coded message below is a quote from Confucius, or Kongfuzi, the Chinese philosopher from the fifth century B.C. Decode the message.

FEVHV QHV FEHVV NHWVYPUEWDU XEWME QHV QPGQYFQAVRLU: Q NHWVYPUEWD XWFE FEV LDHWAEF, XWFE FEV UWYMVHV, QYP XWFE FEV SQY RN SLME RTUVHGQFWRY.

The Domino Effect

The Problem

Games like dominoes have been played in many areas of the world for centuries. Chinese dominoes date back as far as the 12th century A.D. Records show that western dominoes, with which you are probably familiar, were probably not derived from the Chinese. Apparently they were introduced to England by French soldiers in the 18th century. North American Eskimos also play a domino-like game comprised of a set of 148 pieces.

A set of western dominoes has 28 rectangular pieces with two numbers on each one. Each number 0 through 6, is paired with every other number, including itself, on exactly one domino. The grid below was made by arranging the dominoes and then recording the numbers. Four dominoes are shown. Copy the grid and use deductive reasoning to draw in the positions of the remaining dominoes.

1	0	2	0	0	5	4	1
1	1	5	3	6	2	4	2
3	3	1	0	3	5	3	4
0	6	6	4	6	5	1	1
0	4	0	2	5	4	2	6
1	2	3	2	6	4	5	2
3	5	5	0	3	4	6	6

D A T A
SENSE

Looking Ahead

In this unit, you will see how mathematics can be used to answer questions about statistics. You will experience:

▶ representing information using stem-and-leaf plots, frequency tables, histograms, and line plots

▶ measures of center

▶ reading and interpreting bar graphs

▶ making a histogram from data you create in a simulation

▶ recognizing misleading graphs and statistics

Did You Ever Wonder?

What do mathematics and Balzac Balloon Balls have to do with each other? Turn the page and see how Mary A. Rodas of New York City, combined the two!

Teens in the News

Featuring: Mary A. Rodas
Age: 16
Hometown: New York, New York
Career Goal: Politician or Psychiatrist
Interests: yearbook staff, drama

Mary A. Rodas has been telling CATCO Toys what kids like and what kids will buy since she was 14 years old! Now Mary is 16 and Vice President of Marketing for CATCO Inc., a toy company in New York!

Mary has a real knack for making toys fun. In 1989, CATCO was getting ready to come out with the Balzac Balloon Ball. Mary thought it was a great idea, but suggested they add neon graphics to the package and redo the TV commercial to emphasize the balloon inside the ball. Mary is given credit for the $7 million of Balzac Balloon Balls that have been sold worldwide!

Mary has also helped CATCO with two other new products. Deco Discs are cardboard puzzles that you bend and a CD pops out. She also gave advice on a washable slime that you can eat!

Kids who help test CATCO's products aren't afraid to tell Mary what they really think. Mary uses their input to improve the toys and to decide how to price the toys.

Mary has appeared on the Arsenio Hall Show, The Today Show, Good Morning America, and the Dennis Miller Show. She rides from school to work in a limousine. Mary earns a salary and has stock in CATCO Inc. But she has dreams just like any other teen. Mary is saving her money for college. She hopes to become a psychiatrist or a politician.

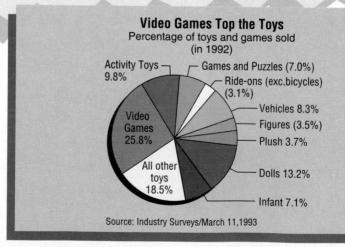

Video Games Top the Toys
Percentage of toys and games sold (in 1992)

- Activity Toys 9.8%
- Games and Puzzles (7.0%)
- Ride-ons (exc. bicycles) (3.1%)
- Vehicles 8.3%
- Figures (3.5%)
- Plush 3.7%
- Dolls 13.2%
- Infant 7.1%
- Video Games 25.8%
- All other toys 18.5%

Source: Industry Surveys/March 11, 1993

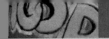

Team Project

Why Buy?

Marketers like Mary Rodas make better decisions when they have good information. A survey is one way to gather information.

You are a marketer for a company that specializes in products for teens. Your company wants to help them to determine how the students at your school spend their money. What questions will you ask? Decide how many students you will survey. Develop the survey and obtain your data. Use a chart or graph to show the results of your survey. What do you suggest for new products at your company?

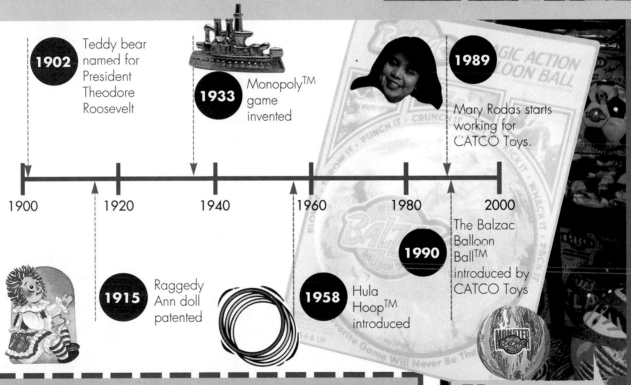

1902 Teddy bear named for President Theodore Roosevelt

1933 Monopoly™ game invented

1989 Mary Rodas starts working for CATCO Toys.

1915 Raggedy Ann doll patented

1958 Hula Hoop™ introduced

1990 The Balzac Balloon Ball™ introduced by CATCO Toys

1900   1920   1940   1960   1980   2000

For more information

If you would like more information about developing new toys, contact:

CATCO Inc.
529 West 42nd Street
New York, New York 10036

You can learn more about the math Mary uses in her job by completing the following activities in this unit.

Setting the Scene

MATHEMATICS TOOLKIT

Many professions require the use of tools. This Mathematics Toolkit includes tools you may find useful during the Data Sense unit. At times you may feel lost or not know where to begin when presented with a problem situation. You should take time to review this toolkit and remember the different statistical tools and problem-solving strategies used by the characters in the following script. You don't need to wait until your teacher tells you to make a chart or find the mean. Instead, if it seems like it might help, try it.

Narrator: Maria, Tran, Asit and Ruth are on the yearbook staff for Jefferson Middle School. They are discussing ideas for a feature article in their yearbook, *The Optimist*.

Maria: Maybe we should do a feature titled "Who is Best Looking?"

Tran: We'd better be careful. We don't want to hurt anyone's feelings.

Asit: The feature page should be cool...we need to attract sales. Let's have something that will include everyone.

Ruth: I've got it. Let's find out what the average seventh grader looks like. That could be our page..."Are you average?"

Maria: I like it! I bet most of our class has brown eyes...

Asit: But, how do we know for sure?

Ruth: We can take a survey, like we did in social studies.

Tran: OK, but what should we ask about besides the color of eyes?

Narrator: The students came up with the following survey.

> **Average Seventh Grader at Jefferson Middle School**
>
> • How tall are you?
>   _____ inches
> • How much do you weigh?
>   _____ pounds
> • What color is your hair?
>   1. Black   2. Brown
>   3. Blonde   4. Red
> • What color are your eyes?
>   1. Brown   2. Hazel
>   3. Blue   4. Green
> • Are you 1. Male or
>   2. Female ?

Narrator: After getting permission from the principal, the students gave the survey to all seventh graders during first period. With all the data collected, the students continued their discussion.

Asit: Now that we have all this data, how are we going to figure out what the average seventh grader looks like?

Ruth: Easy, we just count up all the information.

Maria: I don't think it's that easy. We have all these numbers, but what do we do with them?

Tran: Can't we make this easier?

Ruth: Remember when we did sampling with raisins in math class? We counted a small sample and that told us something about the whole box of raisins.

Tran: So how many should we use?

Narrator: They decided on 25 surveys for their sample. They picked them at random by placing all the surveys in a large box and drawing 25 of them out without looking. Below is the data from that sample.

- How tall are you?
  61, 59, 64, 73, 58, 62, 61, 63, 72, 63, 56, 69, 67, 75, 62, 63, 61, 64, 58, 64, 63, 61, 72, 59, 63

- How much do you weigh?
  121, 89, 171, 97, 195, 139, 103, 194, 148, 109, 100, 112, 115, 118, 80, 124, 129, 102, 145, 106, 168, 169, 117, 110, 101

- What color is your hair?
  1. Black 2. Brown 3. Blonde 4. Red
  1, 3, 1, 1, 2, 2, 4, 1, 2, 1, 1, 3, 3, 1, 2, 4, 1, 1, 1, 3, 3, 2, 2, 1, 2

- What color are your eyes?
  1. Brown 2. Hazel 3. Blue 4. Green
  1, 3, 1, 1, 2, 1, 4, 1, 2, 1, 1, 3, 3, 1, 1, 4, 1, 1, 1, 3, 3, 1, 2, 1, 1

- Are you 1. Male or 2. Female?
  1, 2, 1, 1, 2, 2, 2, 1, 2, 1, 1, 2, 2, 1, 2, 2, 1, 1, 1, 2, 2, 2, 2, 1, 2

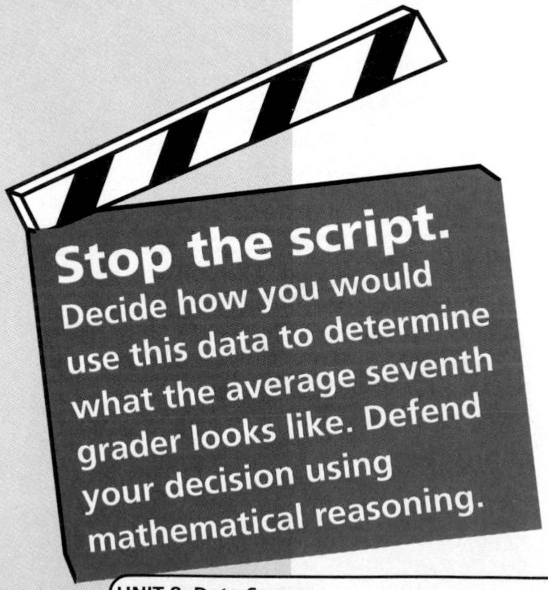

Stop the script.
Decide how you would use this data to determine what the average seventh grader looks like. Defend your decision using mathematical reasoning.

Asit: Let's start with the first question: "How tall are you?"

Tran: I'll make a **stem-and-leaf plot** so we can see what the data looks like. I can use the tens digits as the **stems** and the ones digits as the **leaves**. For example, there are four numbers that have 7 in the tens place. They are 75, 72, 73, and 72. The 5, 2, 3, and 2 are the leaves for the stem 7. So, the number of leaves shows how many values are in each group of ten.

Narrator: Tran creates the stem-and-leaf plot shown below.

tens	ones
5	89698
6	2133349712314143
7	5232

5|8 means 58 inches

Ruth: I don't understand all those numbers all jumbled up like that.

Asit: Well, maybe we can put the leaves in order. Here, I'll do it.

Ruth: Seems right to me. It's what we estimated from the stem-and-leaf plot. Let's analyze the weights now.

Asit: The weights go from 80 to 195 pounds. I think that's going to make a really long stem-and-leaf plot. Maybe we should try a table.

Tran: It looks like we have 25 different weights. A table would be longer than a stem-and-leaf plot!

Maria: We should divide the weights into groups and then tally the weights from the sample.

Narrator: Asit ordered each row of leaves from least to greatest. The result is shown below.

tens	ones
5	68899
6	1111223333344479
7	2235

5|8 means 58 inches

Maria: So... in the first row the numbers are 56, 58, 58, 59, and 59?

Tran: Yeah, you've got the idea.

Ruth: Well, it looks to me like most of this sample is 60-some inches tall. I'd say the average is about 63 or 64 inches.

Asit: But how can we tell for sure?

Maria: How about finding the average? I think it's called the **mean.** You know, you add up all the heights and divide by 25, because we have 25 surveys. Wait, I've got a calculator. The sum of the heights is 1593. 1593 ÷ 25 = 63.72 So the mean height is 63.72 inches.

Ruth: I remember how to make a **frequency table** from math class. First we need to determine a scale for the table. The **scale** must contain all the weights and be separated into equal parts called **intervals.** But before we decide on the intervals, we need to find the **range** of the data by subtracting the lowest weight from the highest weight.

Asit: That would be 195 minus 80. That's 115.

Ruth: The next step is to decide how wide the intervals should be. Interval widths are usually one, ten, one hundred, one thousand, and so on. We should have between 4 and 8 intervals.

Maria: How do we know how many intervals we'll get?

Ruth: We divide the range of the data by the interval width.

Tran: An interval width of 10 means we would need at least 11 intervals.

Ruth: Right, but that's too many intervals.

Asit: How about an interval width of 20? 115 is almost 120 and 120 divided by 20 is 6.

Ruth: Perfect! I'll list the intervals.

Narrator: Ruth makes the following list:
80-99
100-119
120-139
140-159
160-179
180-199

Asit: The scale begins with 80 and ends with 199. That includes all weights in our sample.

Tran: Okay. Let's make the frequency table. Go through the 25 surveys and tally the results.

Narrator: The students make the frequency table shown below.

Interval	Tally	Total
80 - 99	III	3
100 - 119	ℕℕ I	11
120 - 139	IIII	4
140 - 159	II	2
160 - 179	III	3
180 - 199	II	2

Asit: Now that we've created our frequency table, we can use it to create a **histogram.**

Ruth: A histogram?

Maria: It's like a bar graph, only it uses intervals like the ones we used in our frequency table. I'll draw one using the frequency table that we just made.

Narrator: Maria draws the histogram shown below.

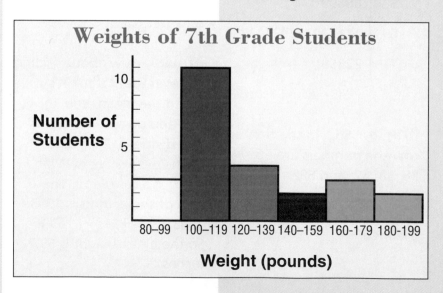

Weights of 7th Grade Students

Number of Students

Weight (pounds)

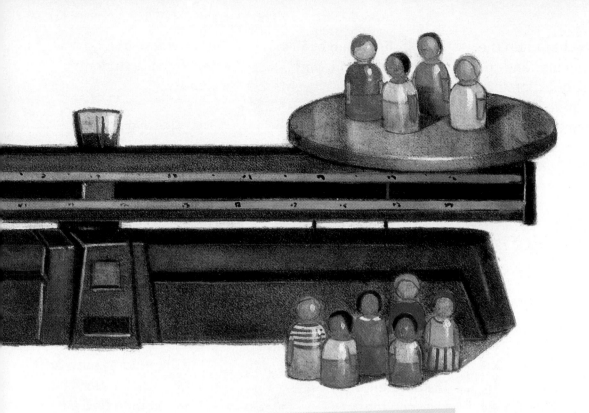

Ruth: Looking at the table and histogram, it looks like the average seventh grader is between 100 -119 pounds, but that range is too big. We need to find only one weight.

Asit: I'll find the mean on the calculator again. The sum of the weights is 3,162. 3,162 ÷ 25 = *126.48* The mean weight is 126.48 pounds.

Tran: 126.48 isn't even in the group with the most people!

Maria: I don't think the mean is right for this data. There are a couple of people who throw the average off. Since the mean weight doesn't even fall in the interval with the most data, maybe we should use the **median**... the weight in the middle.

Tran: Good idea! Let's put the weights in order.
80, 89, 97, 100, 101, 102, 103, 106, 109, 110, 112, 115, 117, 118, 121, 124, 129, 139, 145, 148, 168, 169, 171, 194, 195
Since there are 25 numbers, the 13th number is the middle number. See, it's 117 pounds.

Maria: OK, let's go with 117 pounds as our average weight.

Asit: Next, we have the hair color question. The only numbers we can average are the answer numbers: 1, 2, 3, 4.

Ruth: That doesn't make any sense, especially if we get a fraction answer like $1\frac{1}{5}$.

Maria: Well....what hair color shows up most often? We'll use that as the average.

Narrator: When a value occurs more often than other values in a set of data, we often use that value as an average. That measure is called the **mode**.

Ruth: We should do the same for eye color and the male/female question. I'll make a **line plot** for each of the last three questions.

Narrator: Ruth creates the following line plots.

Hair Color

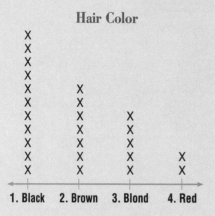

```
X
X
X
X
X      X
X      X
X      X      X
X      X      X
X      X      X
X      X      X      X
X      X      X      X
1. Black  2. Brown  3. Blond  4. Red
```

Eye Color

```
X
X
X
X
X
X
X
X
X             X
X             X
X      X      X
X      X      X      X
X      X      X      X
1. Brown  2. Hazel  3. Blue  4. Green
```

Gender

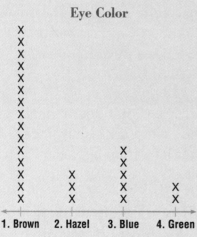

```
                     X
                     X
                     X
              X      X
       X      X
       X      X
       X      X
       X      X
       X      X
       X      X
       X      X
              X
1. Males        2. Females
```

Asit: These line plots clearly show that most students have black hair, brown eyes, and are female.

Maria: I think that the black hair and brown eyes are representative of the students, but the difference between the number of males and females is so small that we shouldn't include gender in the traits of our average seventh grade student.

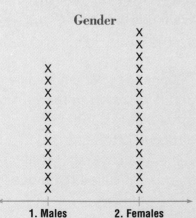

Ruth: I agree, and I don't think we should call this the "average-looking seventh grade student" because most people think that average is always the mean. After all, we only added and divided once to find an average.

Tran: Why don't we change the name to be the "most typical-looking seventh grade student" instead?

Asit: Good idea, but remember this is just a sample of the entire student population. To be really accurate we should evaluate all the data.

Tran: Yeah, we should start that now.

Maria: Wait, before we start I have an idea. We should find all the seventh graders at our school who have all these typical traits, and we can put their pictures on this page.

Ruth: They can be named the "Most Typical Looking Seventh Graders."

Asit: But what about the rest of us?

Tran: We need to show all this data in the yearbook. Remember, it should be interesting to everyone. I know, let's draw graphs of the data on our page. It'll show the entire range of our students.

Maria: We should make histograms from our charts.

Asit: I like it. Now we're all included and we can mark the most typical trait on each graph.

Tran: This is going to be a great page, everyone will want to buy The Optimist this year. We've done a great job!

This concludes the script section of the Mathematics Toolkit. It included many mathematical tools for you to use throughout this unit. As you work through this unit, you should use these tools to help you solve problems. You may want to explain how to use these mathematical tools in your journal. Or you may want to create a toolkit notebook for this purpose.

Mountain Bikes

You are the buyer for a small bike shop. Your decision on which bikes to purchase for the shop is based on knowing how much customers are willing to spend and what the owner can afford to keep in stock. The amount customers will spend on a mountain bike covers a wide range of prices, yet they are all interested in getting the best bike for their money. The owner can afford to carry only three brands of mountain bikes.

You have received a report of tests conducted on the newest models of mountain bikes on the market. Refer to the Mountain Bike Ratings in the Data Bank. Analyze the data and determine which three brands you would recommend that the owner carry. Use mathematical tools and reasoning to defend your recommendations. Be prepared to present your findings to the owner of the bike shop.

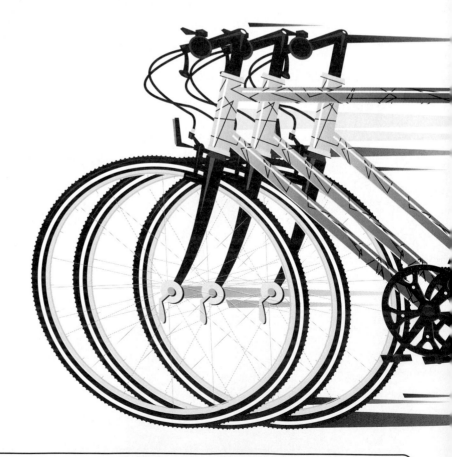

THE EXPANSION BRIDGE
Construction Plan Sheet

1. **Construction Plan:** Each crew must submit a construction plan with a construction budget. This plan should detail the way the bridge is to be built, including an explanation of tasks, strategies, construction methods, resource management, and quality checks. Time, cost, and the degree of cooperation are all equally important.

2. **Construction Budget:** Each construction crew should estimate the amount of construction time needed, determine the amount of raw materials required, and total their cost projection. Labor costs are determined at a rate of $1,000 per minute. Raw materials costs are $100.00 per beam and $7.50 per bolt and nut. These amounts make up the budget.

3. **Acquire Raw Materials:** Once a crew submits a budget, the requested raw materials will be delivered to each team. Each crew will want to verify that all of their requested materials are delivered since no raw materials will be delivered during construction. No excess materials may be sold back after construction begins. Additional materials may not be purchased until after the inspection.

4. **Build Bridge:** Each crew begins construction at a given signal. When a construction crew completes the bridge, the finished time is recorded. Specific roles may be assigned but all must participate in the actual construction of the bridge.

5. **Bridge Inspection:** Each bridge is inspected by an independent inspector after all bridges are built. The inspector guarantees that the bridge is constructed in accordance with the company blueprint. All joints must be securely fastened. If a bridge does not meet the standard, a five-minute delay is charged, and the bridge must be adjusted. The total time accumulates while any revisions are made. An additional delivery fee of $500.00 is added to the raw material fee if any additional materials are needed.

The Expansion Bridge Blueprint

Debriefing Guide

Write a full-page narrative on how your group worked on this expansion bridge simulation. Consider the questions below in writing your narrative. Use them to get started, but don't write only an answer to each question or be limited to just these questions. The narrative will be discussed as a class.

- What methods of construction were considered?
- How did your crew arrive at your estimate?
- Did you follow the plan you developed?
- How was time controlled and quality checked?
- What actions helped/hurt the crew in doing the task?
- How did leadership emerge? Was it shared?
- Were people's individual skills considered?
- Was anyone left out? Were anyone's ideas ignored?
- Was there a sense of satisfaction in building the bridge?
- Would you do anything differently if you could do the construction over again? If so, explain what and why.

THE CONSTRUCTION BID

Below are line plots depicting the construction times, in minutes, of different crews from three different companies. Interpret these line plots. Determine an average construction time for each company to make predictions for future construction jobs. Explain the reasons for your decisions. Make some conjectures (educated guesses) about the construction crews from each company.

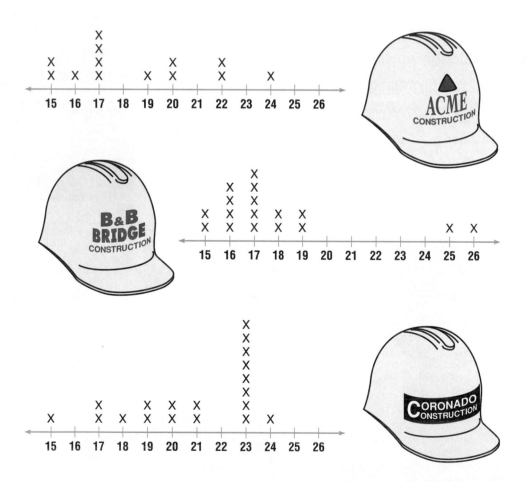

What's the Average?
Mean Median Mode

Read all of the Menu Stations. Choose a station. Be sure that each member of your group examines a different situation.

After selecting a station, determine which measure of center you feel best represents the data in the situation given at your station. Write a statement defending your selection with a convincing argument. Explain why the other measures may be irrelevant or even misleading.

Then take turns with other members of your group discussing the situations at the stations in detail. As a group, decide which station you want to present and defend. Another group or the teacher may state a differing opinion for the situation your group presents. Be prepared to defend your choice.

MENU station A
It Must Be The Shoes!

A trendy, new shoe design is out on the market. Depending on how this design sells, the new shoe is a risky investment for a small shoe store owner like Charlie O'Neill. A wholesaler will allow Mr. O'Neill to purchase one size of this new shoe at a reduced price for a special promotion. The following shoe sizes were collected the last time Mr. O'Neill had a special sale.

Shoe Sizes Sold at Last Sale					
8	7	7	9	11	7
$7\frac{1}{2}$	$8\frac{1}{2}$	7	$10\frac{1}{2}$	6	12
8	7	7	10	$10\frac{1}{2}$	9

1 **D**etermine a measure of center that best represents the shoe sizes.

2 **W**rite a statement justifying your choice.

3 **D**isplay your results in the graphic form that is best for defending your decision.

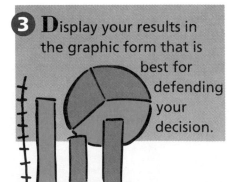

Big Buck$

The vice president of a small company wants to find the "average salary" for the employees of her company. She will use this average salary to make predictions for payroll costs and tax liabilities in preparation for company expansion plans. The payroll manager provided her with the list of salaries below.

$150,000	$90,000	$20,000	$25,000	$90,000	$52,000
$35,000	$90,000	$30,000	$42,000	$42,000	$45,000
$32,000	$20,000	$30,000	$40,000	$25,000	

1 **D**etermine a measure of center that best represents the salaries.

2 **W**rite a statement justifying your choice.

3 **D**isplay your results in the graphic form that is best for defending your decision.

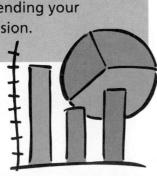

MENU station C

One Size Fits All?

A dress designer for Acme Dress Patterns wants to create a new, unique pattern to use with a revolutionary stretch fabric that has recently become available. This designer believes he can make a lot of money by creating a single pattern that, when used with this new stretchable material, will produce a dress where one size fits all. The pattern should work for all dress sizes with a minimum of stretching or shrinking of the dress. The results of a survey of potential customers are given below.

ACME DRESS PATTERN SIZES

18	12	16	3	6	12
10	6	3	8	10	3
6	8	12	10	3	6
8	8	10	10	6	6

1 **D**etermine the measure of center that best represents the dress sizes.

2 **W**rite a statement justifying your choice.

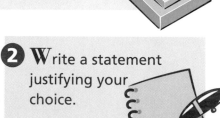

3 **D**isplay your results in the graphic form that is best for defending your decision.

Driving Miss Daily

MENU
station
D

A traveling sales representative, whose territory is Pennsylvania, sells cable TV subscriptions. After every 60,000 miles she travels, she receives a new company car. What follows are the trip odometer readings she logged during the last 24 days. Estimate how many more days until she is entitled to a new company car.

1 Determine the measure of center that best represents the mileage.

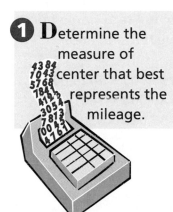

MILEAGE LOG					
180	125	161	39	261	125
310	66	43	89	107	143
96	80	125	10	193	216
178	238	310	170	216	166

2 Write a statement justifying your decision. Then estimate how many more days it will be before she will be entitled to a new company car.

3 Display your results in the graphic form that is best for defending your decision.

MENU station E

Moving Pay

A big corporation is moving to Silicon Valley in California. A number of employees located on the East Coast will be transferring to this new site in San Jose. The company always gives a housing allowance to transferred executives until they sell their previous home. The housing allowance is calculated at 75% of the "average local home price" in the new location. The vice president of human resources wants to find the average home price and a fair housing allowance. A survey of real estate agencies produced the following list of home prices in neighborhoods near this very expensive housing area.

$625,000	$590,000	$460,000	$790,000	$425,000
$1,050,000	$495,000	$495,000	$740,000	$405,000
$860,000	$580,000	$575,000	$495,000	$550,000

1 Determine the measure of center that best represents the home prices.

2 Write a statement justifying your decision.

3 Display your results in the graphic form that is best for defending your decision.

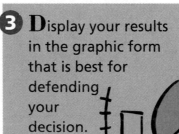

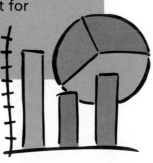

Average News

There are different types of averages. We use these to estimate the center of a set of data. Sometimes the use of one method may give a distorted view of the data.

Look in newspapers or magazines for a real-life example of how one of the averages (measure of center) of a set of data has been determined in order to best understand or use the data. Explain your reasoning. Do you think these measures represent the data in a useful manner?

Super Bowl Scores

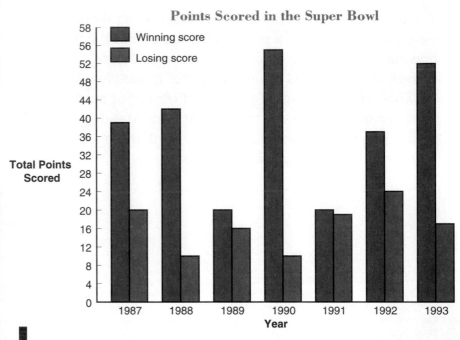

Points Scored in the Super Bowl

- Winning score
- Losing score

Total Points Scored (vertical axis: 0, 4, 8, 12, 16, 20, 24, 28, 32, 36, 40, 44, 48, 52, 56, 58)

Year (horizontal axis): 1987, 1988, 1989, 1990, 1991, 1992, 1993

Interpret the bar graph above. Explain in detail all of the elements of the graph. Include statistical measures. Use mathematics to create additional information from the graph.

Summarize what the graph shows and state any conclusions or trends regarding Super Bowl scores that you have derived from the data generated.

Refer to the "Life in the United States" graphs in the Data Bank or find an example of a bar graph in a newspaper, magazine, or from some other source.

Write a paragraph interpreting the bar graph. Be sure to explain the subject of the graph, each scale, and any conclusions the reader might draw from the graph.

American Railbridges

American Railbridges builds trusses used to support railroad bridges throughout the world. The company is the largest construction company of its kind, but they have a reputation of slow completion times. Below is a histogram that illustrates the amount of time it took construction crews to complete the last 158 trusses.

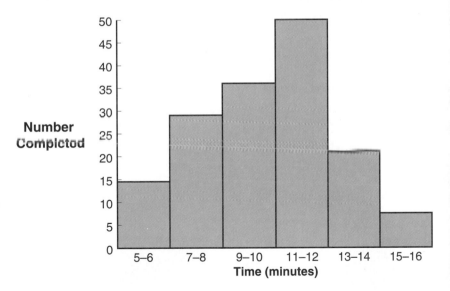

American Railbridges Construction Times

Number Completed (y-axis)

Time (minutes) (x-axis): 5–6, 7–8, 9–10, 11–12, 13–14, 15–16

- With your partner, discuss and interpret the histogram above and be ready to share your ideas with the class.
- Describe what the graph might look like if the crews were able to complete the trusses at a much faster rate.

Truss Time

Your class has been hired by the management team of a new competitor to American Railbridges. Your company's first contract is to build at least 30 trusses. You and your classmates have been hired as new construction crews. Below is the blueprint for a truss. Each crew should build these trusses as quickly as possible, insuring quality work. After the completion time is recorded, each crew will disassemble their truss. Then each crew will rebuild a truss to see if they can better their time.

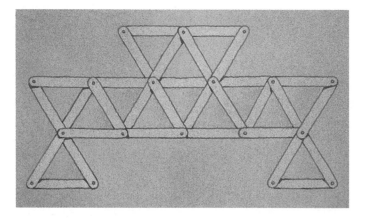

After analyzing the construction times, the management team believes that your company can gain new truss contracts by showing how your crews outperformed the crews from American Railbridges. Using your company's times, design a histogram that will help promote your company to potential customers.

Newark News

Examine and compare the advertisements below.

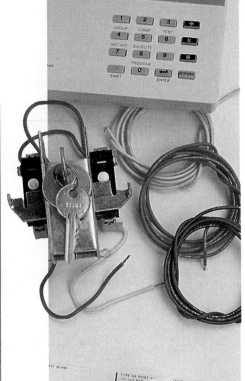

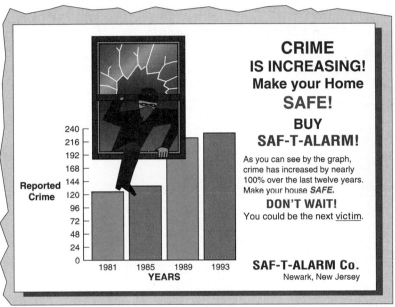

CRIME IS INCREASING!
Make your Home SAFE!
BUY SAF-T-ALARM!

As you can see by the graph, crime has increased by nearly 100% over the last twelve years. Make your house *SAFE*.

DON'T WAIT!
You could be the next <u>victim</u>.

SAF-T-ALARM Co.
Newark, New Jersey

Reported Crime

240
216
192
168
144
120
96
72
48
24
0

1981 1985 1989 1993
YEARS

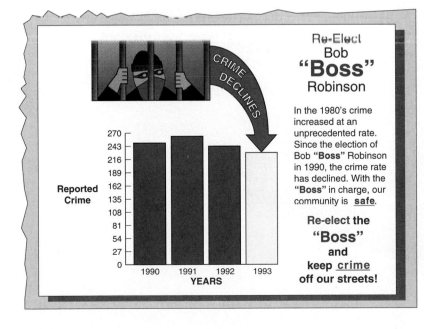

Re-Elect
Bob
"Boss"
Robinson

CRIME DECLINES

In the 1980's crime increased at an unprecedented rate. Since the election of Bob **"Boss"** Robinson in 1990, the crime rate has declined. With the **"Boss"** in charge, our community is <u>**safe**</u>.

Re-elect the "Boss"
and
keep <u>crime</u> off our streets!

Reported Crime

270
243
216
189
162
135
108
81
54
27
0

1990 1991 1992 1993
YEARS

Both advertisements, *Crime Increases* and *Crime Declines*, appeared in the Newark News, September 24, 1994. They used data from the same source, yet the information presented was very different.

Discuss the advertisements in your group. As a group, submit a letter to the editor explaining how the graphs were drawn to influence the readers and explain how the information was manipulated to make the advertisers' points.

Every Picture Tells a Story

Design a travel brochure describing the temperature a tourist can expect in San Diego during the summer. Be sure to make your brochure attractive to the clients who frequently use your travel agency. Use a histogram and other information to persuade clients to travel to San Diego.

The high temperatures recorded each day in San Diego during the months of July and August, measured in degrees Fahrenheit, are given below.

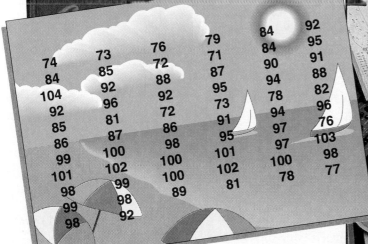

			79	84	92
74	73	76	71	84	95
84	85	72	87	90	91
104	92	88	95	94	88
92	96	92	73	78	82
85	81	72	91	94	96
86	87	86	95	97	76
99	100	98	101	97	103
101	102	100	102	100	98
98	99	100	81	78	77
99	98	89			
98	92				

COMPUTER investigation

Homerun Consultants

You work with a scouting/consulting firm for Major League Baseball. General managers from various teams hire your company to analyze and make recommendations for acquiring new players.

Your company is noted for using statistics to recommend players. You have been the most successful scouting/consulting firm because you use the most modern technology.

A major league team is planning to improve their team next season. Last year, this team was in last place and now needs talent for all positions and in all areas of the game. Both hitters and pitchers are needed to help turn the team around.

Your company has been given the statistics of the forty players who are available. The team requests that your company submit two detailed recommendation reports, one on hitters and the other on pitchers. Break your firm into two pairs, with one pair rating the pitchers and the other rating the hitters.

YOUR REPORT

Each consultant pair should refer to the Baseball Formulas in the Data Bank and write a detailed report, rating the players on their list and giving a statistical argument explaining the players' rating. Graphs, spreadsheet printouts, data lists, and specific information is required in the report along with detailed recommendations and supporting statistical arguments. Each consultant pair will present and defend their findings to the class.

Table Talk

Similar to the mountain bike or baseball player activity, this investigation involves choosing a topic, finding data, and displaying it in a table. After you select a topic and know where or how to find the data, write a statement of need or a problem to solve using the data. For example, remember that

in previous activities the need or problem was to select the top three mountain bikes and to rank the baseball players.

There are many sources of topics and data. Many of these sources are available in libraries. A few suggested sources are periodicals, (*Consumer Reports, Money, Business Week, Newsweek, Sports Illustrated,* and so on), consumer catalogs, almanacs, electronic bulletin boards, or data bases. This data could be consumer products, economic information, sport statistics, or social data. Below are some topic ideas that might get you thinking, but don't feel you need to pick from this list!

What is the best CD player to buy?
Where is the best place to live?
Rank the top ten vacation spots.
Who is the best basketball player ever to play?
Rank the best clothes stores.
What is the typical "family" like?

Select a topic and write a statement describing the need to analyze the data or a problem to solve using the data. Next, organize the data in a table. There must be at least 60 rows in the table.

Select what you feel is the most important criteria for the problem. Interview someone outside of school and ask them which criteria or category is most important to them considering the problem situation.

Analyze the data. Use statistical measures to help rate and compare the data. Determine your findings and conclusions.

Write a detailed report describing your process and conclusions. Make the report persuasive. Use graphs and/or histograms to support your findings.

Write a summary of the process you used in completing this report.

This project is the major assessment for this unit. You may need to do considerable work on this investigation outside of class.

A completed report should include:

- A description of the topic to be analyzed, rated, or ranked.
- A background statement regarding the topic.
- A statement of the need or problem to solve that relates to the topic studied.
- A rationale for choosing the topic.
- A complete list of the data you gathered and the source of the data (minimum of 60 items).
- An explanation of the analysis of the data.
- A description of statistical measures and tools used in analyzing the data.
- A description of the criteria used to analyze the data.
- An interview of someone outside of school on the criteria for analyzing the data.
- All conclusions and findings.
- Statistical graphs depicting the data and supporting your conclusions.
- A summary of the process you used in completing this task.

Selection and Reflection

A student transferred to class near the end of the Data Sense unit. He was assigned to your group and you already know you're going to like working with him. He doesn't have a clue about all the statistical measures and tools you've been using. You offer to help him by listing and describing the statistical measures and tools you've used in the unit. It might help him if you use the tasks in the unit to illustrate your explanation.

In your explanation, you may want to compare the effectiveness of the measures and tools in those situations. What would you say to this student? Write your answer on a separate piece of paper.

Books of the Month

The Problem

Conduct a survey of 20 of your classmates to determine how many books each student read last month. Based on the results of your survey, answer the following questions.

- What is the least number of books read? the greatest number?
- What would the best "average" of the data be? Why?
- Is the data spread out or clustered together? What does this mean?
- If you wanted to use this data to encourage students to read more books, how would you do it? Design a poster or develop a campaign to promote reading.

The Problem

Andrew Cafaro, a professional baseball player, is planning to ask his manager for a raise based on his performance improvements in the past year. Below are his batting statistics for 1993 and 1994.

	1993	1994
Hits	151	144
At Bats	420	396

Should Andrew receive a raise based on these statistics?

Batting a Thousand?

Extension If Andrew is at bat 405 times in 1995, how many hits would he have to make to improve over his 1994 batting average?

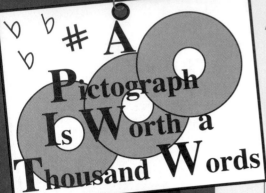

The Problem

A pictograph is a graph that uses pictures or symbols to represent statistical data. The pictographs below are similar to bar graphs, but they use a series of musical notes instead of solid bars to represent the data. Notice that the key tells you that each musical note represents ten units sold.

Music Mania's November Sales

Rock

Pop

Country

Classical

Key: Compact Disc   Cassette Tape   ♪ = Ten Units sold

- Which are more popular: CDs or tapes? How do you know?

- Which type of music is most popular? How do you know?

- Think of three other symbols or pictures you could use to illustrate the data above.

Extension Write some reasons why CDs may be more popular for certain types of music and why tapes may be more popular for other types of music.

The Problem

Nearly eight million American teens do some sort of volunteer work, anything from visiting the elderly to coaching sports to repairing playground equipment. They don't get paid for this work, so why do they do it? The bar graph below gives you an idea.

Why Teens Volunteer

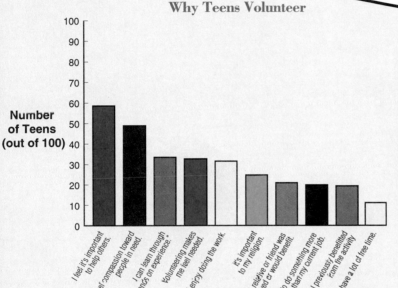

Number of Teens (out of 100)

Teens could choose more than one answer   Source: Independent Sector survey, 1992

- What is the most popular reason why teens volunteer?

- How many teens out of 100 volunteer because they enjoy doing the work? What percent is this?

The Problem

Katrina is taking seventh grade math. Her test scores for the first half of the year are 93, 60, 99, 72, 80, 96, 95, and 91. If Katrina wants to brag about how well she is doing in math, which "average" would she use? Is this average an accurate representation of her grades? Explain.

The Problem

What is your favorite potato chip? A group of professionally trained food tasters came up with the results shown in the chart below. The brands are listed in the order of tastiness.

Which Chip?

CHIP PICKS
(The brands are listed in order of tastiness.)

Very Good	Price per ounce
Lady Lee	14¢
Cape Cod	20¢
Jays	18¢
Cape Cod Unsalted	20¢
Eagle Idaho Russet	23¢
Albertsons	12¢
Ruffles	21¢
Lay's Crunch Taters	23¢
Vons	13¢

Good	
Ruffles Light	25¢
Kroger	12¢
Wise	17¢
Charles Chips	21¢
Pringles Original	21¢
Lay's	21¢
Pringles Light Original	24¢
Golden Flake	17¢
Pathmark	10¢
Michael Season's	28¢
Wise Cottage Fries	21¢
Pringles Idaho Rippled Original	22¢
Barrel O'Fun	20¢
New York Deli	24¢
Keebler Ripplin's	19¢
O'Boisie's	25¢
Lay's Unsalted	21¢

Fair	
Munchos	34¢
Keebler Tato Skins	15¢

Poor	
Mr. G's Old-Fashioned	17¢

Source: *Zillions*, June/July 1991

- In which category do most of the chips fall?

- Does a higher price necessarily mean a better tasting chip?

- Suppose you are the owner of Albertson's grocery stores. You produce your own brand of potato chips, called Albertson's potato chips. You want to convince people to buy your chips. How could you use the information in the chart and any conclusions based on this information to sell your potato chips?

On your feet!

The Problem

Record the number of students in your math class. Then record those who are wearing athletic shoes and what type of athletic shoe they are wearing. Group these by categories such as the ones shown in the diagram below. Next, find out the approximate number of students in your school.

Use your classroom data and the number of students in your school to predict how many students would be wearing each type of athletic shoe.

SNEAKER SEARCH

Here are some of the ways sneakers can differ-

TENNIS: Extra flexibility at ball of foot, extra side-to-side support, reinforced toe.

CROSS-TRAINERS: A combination of features that suits general sports activity, but not serious sports activity.

AEROBICS/FITNESS: Light weight, extra flexibility, light weight sole.

BASKETBALL: Extra side-to-side support, can come in high top versions, rugged soles.

RUNNING: Light weight, extra heel stability, breathable materials.

DON'T FENCE ME IN

Looking Ahead

In this unit, you will see how mathematics can be used to answer questions about perimeter and area. You will experience:

▶ investigating relationships between the perimeter and the area of different geometric shapes

▶ creating spreadsheets to compare the areas of various rectangles

▶ estimating the area of irregular shapes

▶ finding the area of triangles and parallelograms

▶ finding the probability of events

Did You Ever Wonder?

What do mathematics and lawn mowers have to do with each other? Turn the page and see how David C. Eilers of Roswell, Georgia, combined the two!

 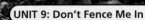

Teens in the News

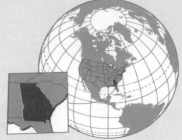

Featuring: David C. Eilers
Age: 17
Hometown: Roswell, Georgia
Career Goal: Horticultural Specialist
Interests: business

When David Eilers was 10 years old, he started a mowing business. David mowed lawns for eight customers. His dad helped him get a business loan, and David got more equipment and more customers. **DAVID'S MOWING SERVICE** grew from making $16,000 a year to making $49,000 a year by the time David was only 15!

David changed the name of his business to **GREEN SEASONS.** His crews would mow lawns while he was in school and on Saturdays David would work 12 hours. The crews were mostly guys in their twenties and thirties. Sometimes he had trouble getting them to pay attention to him. David would make sure that the work was done exactly as the customers wanted. Eventually David got a few good crews.

David handled all the business details for **GREEN SEASONS**. He would figure the area of each lawn to know how much to charge each customer. He had to determine what percentage of nitrogen, phosphorus acid, and potassium each lawn needed. He used a computer spreadsheet to help him with the customer billings.

David has taken a break in business while going to North Metro Technical Institute in Georgia. He says running his own business was fun. He even earned the respect of the twenty- and thirty-year-olds who worked on his crews!

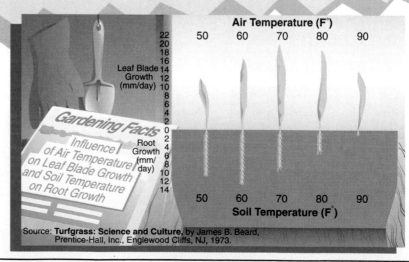

Source: **Turfgrass: Science and Culture,** by James B. Beard, Prentice-Hall, Inc., Englewood Cliffs, NJ, 1973.

Team Project

Four Seasons

A business like David's is called *seasonal*. That means his business depends upon the season of the year. What services could David add to make **GREEN SEASONS** a year-round business? How could he let current customers know about these new services? How could he get new customers? How should David charge customers for these services? Should some charges be based on time and others on measurements like perimeter and area?

Help David come up with a plan to make **GREEN SEASONS** a year-round business.

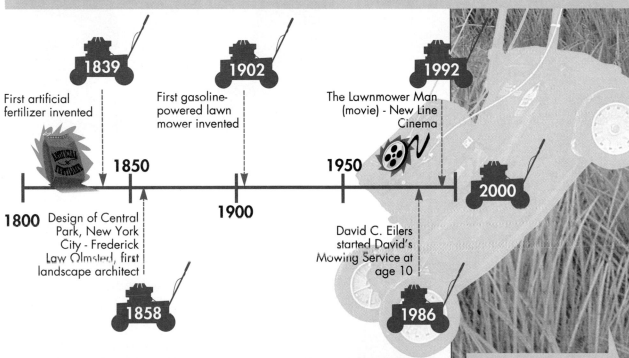

1839 First artificial fertilizer invented

1902 First gasoline-powered lawn mower invented

1992 The Lawnmower Man (movie) - New Line Cinema

1850

1800 Design of Central Park, New York City - Frederick Law Olmsted, first landscape architect

1858

1900

1950

David C. Eilers started David's Mowing Service at age 10

1986

2000

For more information

If you would like more information about starting your own business, contact:

ASSOCIATION FOR CORPORATE GROWTH
55 Park Place
Atlanta, Georgia 30335

Y̶ou can learn more about the math David used in his lawn care service by completing the activities in this unit.

Setting the Scene

MATHEMATICS TOOLKIT

Many professions require the use of tools. This mathematics toolkit includes the tools you will need in the Don't Fence Me In unit. At times you may feel lost or not know where to begin when presented with a problem situation. You should take time to review this toolkit and remember the different tools and problem-solving strategies used by the characters in the following script. You don't need to wait until your teacher gives you a hint. Instead, if an approach seems like it will work, try it!

Narrator: Carla, Jane, Bo, and Bill are members of the environmental club at Colina Intermediate School. They are discussing a recycling project.

Bill: We've found a company that will recycle old phone books. What should we do now?

Carla: First of all, we need to decide what we are going to put the phone books in when people bring them in.

Jane: Right! We need to know how big the phone books are.

Bo: Do you mean how big around they are or how much area they cover?

Bill: I think we mean how much area, not perimeter.

Bo: What's perimeter?

Bill: **Perimeter** means the distance around the outside of a figure. Like the distance around a border. **Area** is the number of square units needed to cover a surface.

Bo: Okay, we need the area. How do we do that?

Jane: We get the dimensions first.

Bo: Okay, what does that mean?

Carla: It means we need the length and width of a phone book.

Bo: So how does that help us find the area?

Bill: Now that we have the area of the bottom of a phone book, how large do our storage containers need to be? Will it work to use anything that has the same area on the bottom?

Jane: Good question! It really needs to have the same dimensions so that the phone books will fit inside. Let's all measure and see what size we get!

Bill: So let's measure. We need to get a ruler.

Jane: I have one. Here, measure across the top and then down one side. That will give us its length and width.

Carla: The phone book has the shape of a rectangle. To find the area of a rectangle, all you do is multiply the length times the width.

Stop the Script!
Determine what size container the students should obtain. Defend your decision using mathematical reasoning.

Narrator: After the students decide on the container, their attention turns to other concerns.

Carla: How many phone books do you think we will get in a week? The recycling company told us that most schools have about 75% of their students participate.

Jane: Gee, I don't know. Let's just think about what would happen if 75% of the students bring in one phone book every week.

Bo: Wow! That would be a bunch of phone books. How many kids are in school?

Bill: Well, we have about 600 students, so...

Carla: This is going to be a lot of phone books. The recycling company said they would come to the school to get them when we have at least 5,000 phone books. How many weeks will that take?

Stop the Script!
Determine how long it will take to collect at least 5,000 phone books.

Narrator: The students start to determine the number of weeks it will take to collect 5,000 phone books.

Carla: So if 75% of the students bring in one phone book this week, how many will we have by Friday?

Bo: Well, we just multiply 75% times the number of students in the school.

Jane: Right. But how do you multiply using the percent sign?

Carla: I remember when we did this in math class. You write 75% as a decimal by moving the decimal point two places to the left. Then you can use a calculator to find the product.

0.75 ⊠ 600 ⊟ 450

So, we should have about 450 phone books by Friday.

Bo: Is that right?

Bill: Another way to look at it is that 75% equals $\frac{3}{4}$. Like 75 cents is three quarters. Anyway, half of 600 is 300 and half again, which is one-fourth, is 150. So, three-fourths is 150 times 3 or 450. See we have it right!

Jane: Let's make a graph to represent the number of phone books we collect each week to see when it reaches over 5,000.

Bill: Good idea. We'll need to make a line graph to show the total we have at the end of each week.

Bo: Okay, we'll graph it like ordered pairs in the coordinate plane, but change our scale.

Jane: Show us what you mean.

Bo: Let the x-axis represent the number of weeks and let the y-axis represent the number of phone books in thousands. The first week we'll have about 450 phone books so we put a point at (1, 450).

Narrator: Bo draws the graph shown below.

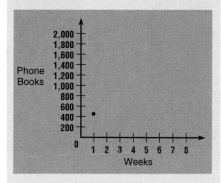

Bill: Okay, so then what happens the second week?

Bo: Well, how many phone books total should we have at the end of the second week?

Bill: 900?

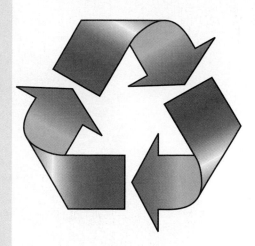

Bo: Right, so we would have a point at the ordered pair (2, 900) like this.

Narrator: Bo adds the point to the graph. The result is shown below.

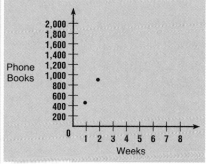

Carla: I think I see what to do!

Stop the Script!
Plot the cumulative totals for the next five weeks.

Narrator: The group plots the points representing the totals for each of the next five weeks. The result is shown below.

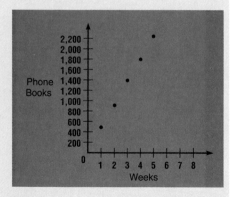

Carla: Hey, these points make a line. Let's just extend the line.

Bo: Yeah! It's crossing between the eleventh and twelfth weeks. In fact, we'll be over just a bit on the twelfth week.

Jane: Let's put our graph on the wall and show the school how many phone books we need to reach our goal. Maybe it will help everyone remember.

Bill: What if they get papers or bulletins sent to their homes and they want to recycle them?

Carla: I guess it is okay if they fit in our containers.

Jane: And the recycling company will take them.

Bo: Okay, so are we saying anything smaller is okay?

Jane: Yeah, so let's let everyone know the perimeter of our box.

Carla: Will the perimeter do or should we tell them the actual dimensions?

Bill: Are there items with the same perimeter that wouldn't fit in our container?

Bo: I think so. What if they were much longer and really narrow? Wouldn't that work - or not work - I should say!

This concludes the Mathematics Toolkit. It included many mathematical tools for you to use throughout this unit. As you work through this unit, you should use these tools to help you solve problems. You may want to explain how to use these mathematical tools in your journal. Or you may want to create a toolkit notebook to add mathematical tools you discover throughout this unit.

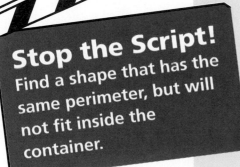

Stop the Script!
Find a shape that has the same perimeter, but will not fit inside the container.

LAND OF THE LAKES

You work in the public relations office for the state's Natural Resources Department. After a mild winter, the fish population in two of the state's lakes has become too large for each lake's food supply to support. If the fish population is not decreased, many fish will die of starvation. You are preparing a press release that you hope will encourage people who fish to visit these two lakes and help reduce the overcrowding. You want to mention the size of these lakes in your press release.

Refer to the Lake Shore Drawings in your Data Bank. Prepare a brief report explaining why each lake might be considered larger. Describe how you might estimate the sizes of these two lakes.

PERENNIALS' PERIMETER

You are a landscape architect for Lance Caper and Associates, a landscape design and construction firm. The owner has given you the letter shown below and assigned this project to your design team. Using the information in the letter, determine the amount of raw material needed and create scale drawings. Be prepared to present your proposal to the mayor.

Dear Mr. Lance Caper,

The Greentree City Council voted to have the grounds of our community center professionally landscaped. We would like to have a patio built out of southwestern tiles that are one foot square. In addition, we have received some very rare and valuable plants that we would like to use as a border for the patio. If planted 1 foot apart, the plants will extend 57 feet. I would like you to submit five different plans for a patio for the community center that would use one-foot-square-tiles and all of the plants. We will have a 3-foot wide walk from the community center to the patio. Otherwise we want plants all around the patio.

I am uncertain about whether the patio should have a large or small area, so I would appreciate your submitting plans that might cover a wide variety of areas if that is possible.

Sincerely,

Iris Flowers

Iris Flowers
Mayor of Greentree

Patio Pointers

Suppose you are asked to design a patio that has a perimeter of 100 feet. The client wants the patio to have square tiles with sides that are one foot long.

- How would you arrange the tiles to get a patio with the smallest area?
- What would that area be?
- How would you arrange the tiles to get a patio with the largest area?
- What would that area be?

Using what you have discovered, could you find the smallest and largest rectangular area for any given perimeter? Explain how you could find those areas.

For rectangles, is there always a limit to the smallest and largest area for any given perimeter? Explain your answer.

B.A. Gardener

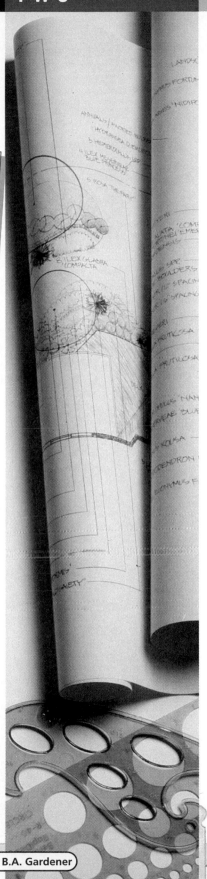

Dear Lance Caper,

I would like to plant a flower garden at the community center. I have determined that I could maintain an area of 60 square feet. I was wondering if you could help me design the garden. I will plant the flowers in rows that need to be one foot apart. I would also like to protect the flowers from animals by enclosing the garden with a fence. Please submit five different proposals that would take into account all of these requirements.

Sincerely,

B. A. Gardener

B.A. Gardener

Use the planning guidelines below to reply to B.A. Gardener.

Garden Planning Guidelines

Garden Proposal: Each design team must submit plans for five different gardens that meet the requirements specified in B. A. Gardener's letter. Each of these should be scale drawings on centimeter grid paper.

Cost: Although B. A. Gardener has not expressed concern over the cost of the garden, from experience you know that all consumers ultimately take cost into consideration. The garden will be enclosed using a small white picket fence that will cost $4.98 per foot. Calculate the cost of fence for each garden in your presentation.

Presentation of Proposals: Each design team will present their proposals in a public hearing to be attended by all other design teams. It is important that each member of your design team understand your drawings and be able to answer questions.

RING AROUND THE ROSES

S uppose you are asked to design a rectangular flower garden that has an area of 100 square feet. The client wants to be able to measure the length and width of the surrounding fence in feet.

- How would you arrange the fence to get a garden with the smallest perimeter?
- What would that perimeter be?
- How would you arrange the fence to get a garden with the largest perimeter?
- What would that perimeter be?

Using what you have discovered, could you find the smallest and largest perimeter for any given area? Explain how you could find those perimeters.

For rectangles, is there always a limit to the smallest and largest perimeter for any given area? Explain your answer.

The Royal Rule

In the kingdom of Squareless, an edict was issued that called for everyone to give a parcel of land to the Queen. The Queen declared that the land had to be no smaller than that which could be enclosed by 28 meters of fence, and no side could be less than one meter long. Most of the people in the kingdom simply gave the Queen a square plot of land that was seven meters on each side.

One very clever member of the kingdom decided to give the Queen as little land as possible and was able to comply with the Queen's edict by giving only 13 square meters of land. When the Queen learned of this, she was outraged and sent for the man. When the man arrived, the Queen told him that he was sentenced to life in prison for outsmarting the Queen.

The clever man quickly asked the Queen if the sentence could be suspended if he could truly amaze the Queen. The Queen, being quite egotistical, agreed.

The clever man showed the Queen the drawing below. Each square represents parcels of land that measure 1 meter on each side. He asked the Queen how much fence it would take to fence the area shown. The Queen quickly calculated the correct response. The clever man then told the Queen that he could increase the area by 50% and still enclose it with the same amount of fence.

The Queen was quite puzzled. She told the clever man that a clear explanation of the solution to this problem would ensure his freedom.

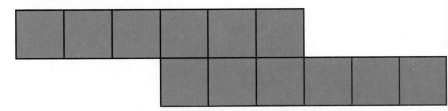

1. Using centimeter grid paper, draw a model of the plot of land most people gave to the Queen. Then draw a model of the plot of land the clever man gave to the Queen.

2. Using centimeter grid paper, draw the shape made by the clever man shown at the bottom of the previous page. How many more squares can you enclose and not change the perimeter? Will the clever man's sentence be suspended? Explain why or why not.

3. Are you clever too?

   a. Draw a shape similar to the one drawn by the clever man that has a perimeter of 18. How can you increase the area by 75% without changing the perimeter?

   b. Draw a shape that has a perimeter of 14. Double the area without changing the perimeter.

   c. Draw a shape that has a perimeter of 20. Show how the area can more than double without changing the perimeter.

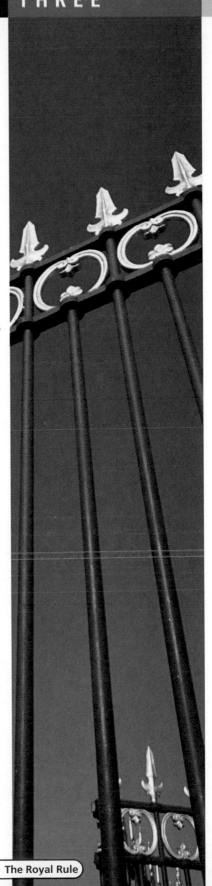

Suppose the Queen wanted you to fence in a rectangular space that had a perimeter of 28 meters. What are the possible rectangular dimensions? Make a list of at least five examples.

What has to be true of each of the pairs of dimensions that you find? Write a statement to justify your answer.

Using the top graph of Blackline Master 10-3, plot the possible dimensions as ordered pairs.

Connect the points. Describe what is formed.

Suppose the Queen wanted you to fence in a rectangular space that had an area of 28 square meters. What are the possible rectangular dimensions? Make a list of at least five examples.

What has to be true of each of the pairs of dimensions that you find? Write a statement to justify your answer.

Using the bottom graph on Blackline Master 10-3, plot the possible dimensions as ordered pairs.

Connect the points. Describe what is formed.

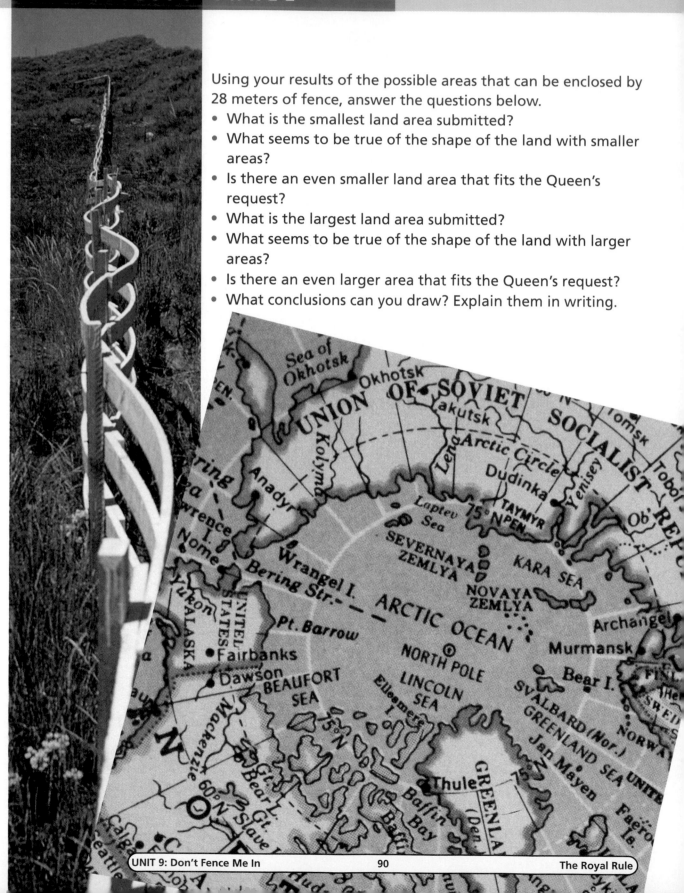

Using your results of the possible areas that can be enclosed by 28 meters of fence, answer the questions below.

- What is the smallest land area submitted?
- What seems to be true of the shape of the land with smaller areas?
- Is there an even smaller land area that fits the Queen's request?
- What is the largest land area submitted?
- What seems to be true of the shape of the land with larger areas?
- Is there an even larger area that fits the Queen's request?
- What conclusions can you draw? Explain them in writing.

The Clever Man's Challenge!

After the clever man managed to successfully escape being imprisoned by the Queen, he decided to issue his own challenge.

> Your Majesty, if this is really the kingdom of Squareless, why do you insist that all of the parcels of land be squares or rectangles? If I simply gave you 28 meters of fencing and no restrictions, what would be the greatest land area you could enclose? I challenge you to break out of your mold!

Cut a piece of string that is 28 cm long. Tape the string on centimeter grid paper in a manner that encloses the largest area possible. Determine a method for estimating the area you have enclosed and then find the area using your method. Be prepared to discuss how you determined the areas.

HOME ON THE RANGE

Big Tex has a home on the range (where the deer and the antelope play). He has also built a barn in which to keep his horses. The dimensions of the barn are 80 feet by 120 feet.

Big Tex has a problem. He wants to fence in a rectangular shaped space where his horses can exercise, but he can only afford to buy 170 feet of fencing. His whole farm has been fenced with wire, but he wants to use nice wooden fencing for the exercise corral. What would be the largest area he could enclose for his horses using 170 feet of fencing?

- Big Tex has hired you to submit plans to him that show ways he can fence in an exercise area for his horses. He has made it quite clear that he wants a rectangular space with the largest area possible. Use your grid paper to design a scale drawing of what the area would look like and calculate the enclosed area.

- You know that Big Tex is always looking for a deal. In working on his fence problem, you discover a way to fence in a space with a larger area using the same amount of fencing, if you don't have to make a rectangle. Make a scale drawing of what the space would look like and calculate the area. Prepare an argument that you would present to Big Tex.

- Consider how large an area you could enclose if you fenced in a rectangular space using the side of Big Tex's barn as one of the sides. What is the greatest area you can now enclose?

Write a formula that represents the perimeter of the fenced area using the barn. What part of the formula represents the fence and what part represents the barn?

Corral Clues

If you have 140 feet of fence and a building that is 80 feet long, how could you best use your fence?

Make a chart or a scale drawing and explore possible answers.

Do you have the same relationship between width and length that you had in Big Tex's fence problem?

When you first wanted to enclose a rectangular area without using the side of the barn or building, what shape did you discover had the largest area?

How can you use that information to find the dimensions of the rectangle that will have the largest area using the side of a barn or a building?

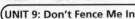

Keyboard Corrals

Many businesses use computers to help them organize and analyze data. One of the most widely used applications is called a **spreadsheet**. A spreadsheet program creates a large arrangement of boxes called **cells,** each of which has its own **address**. In most spreadsheet programs, the address consists of a letter and a numeral to indicate the respective column and row in which the cell is located. A cell may contain numbers, words (called labels), or a formula. Let's examine how a spreadsheet could be used to solve Big Tex's fencing problem.

Headings are usually entered in row 1. Sample headings for Big Tex's fence problem are shown below.

	A	B	C	D	E
1	AMOUNT OF FENCE	LENGTH OF BARN	LENGTH OF CORRAL	WIDTH OF CORRAL	AREA OF CORRAL
2					
3					

Suppose you tell the computer the amount of fence you have and the length of the barn. Let's see how you might tell the computer to calculate the numbers in the remaining columns. Examine the spreadsheet below.

	A	B	C	D	E
1	AMOUNT OF FENCE	LENGTH OF BARN	LENGTH OF CORRAL	WIDTH OF CORRAL	AREA OF CORRAL
2	170	120	90	40.0	3600.0
3	170	120	89	40.5	3604.5
4	170	120	88	41.0	3608.0
5	170	120	87	41.5	3610.5
6	170	120			

Do you see a pattern developing? Use this pattern and cell addresses to write a formula for cells C6, D6, and E6.

The Shape of Things to Come

Hands Down

1 **W**ith your fingers together, draw an outline of your hand on a sheet of centimeter grid paper. Estimate the area of the figure. Record your estimate.

2 **W**rite a statement explaining the procedure you used to estimate the area of your hand.

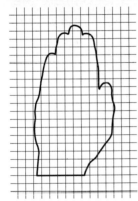

3 **D**isplay your findings in the graphic form that you think is best for supporting your findings.

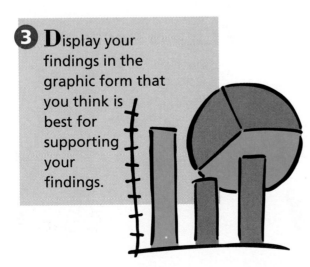

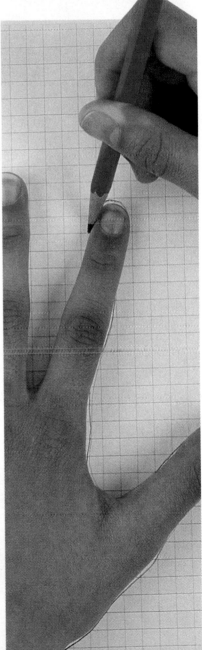

MENU
station
B

JIGSAW PUZZLED

1 **T**race the outline of the same jigsaw puzzle piece in two different places on a piece of centimeter grid paper. Estimate the area of the figure. Record your estimate.

2 **U**sing the two illustrations below, develop a method for estimating the area of the puzzle piece shown. Then use this newly developed method to estimate the area of the puzzle piece you traced in step 1. Compare the result to your original estimate.

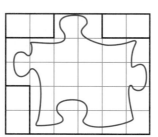 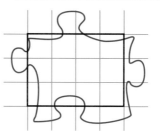

3 **W**rite a statement explaining the method you developed for estimating the area of your jigsaw puzzle piece.

GEOBOARD BOUND

MENU
s t a t i o n

1 Use a geoboard and a geoband to form a rectangle. Use another geoband to connect the lower left-hand corner of the rectangle with the upper right-hand corner.

2 Describe the two shapes that are formed. How do they compare?

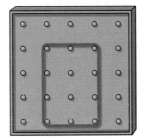

3 Find the area of the original rectangle. What is the area of each triangle?

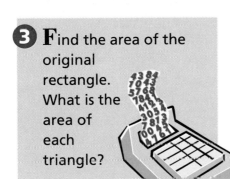

4 Repeat steps 1, 2, and 3 for several different rectangles.

5 Prepare a concluding report identifying a method for finding the area of a triangle that does not involve counting squares. Include illustrations to support your conclusions.

MENU station D

CONNECT THE DOTS

Use the recording sheet your teacher gives you for this station.

Make these triangles on your geoboard.

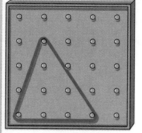
Triangle 1

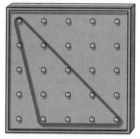
Triangle 2

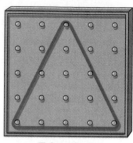
Triangle 3

1 **F**ind the area of each triangle. Record your findings in Column B of the recording sheet.

2 **D**evelop a method for finding the area of a triangle that involves pegs that are enclosed by the geoband. You may use columns B, C, and D of the recording sheet to help in the development of your method.

3 **U**se the method you developed in step 2 to find the area of several different polygons. Record your results on the recording sheet.

4 **W**rite a summary report about any conclusions you made during this activity.

SHAPE UP!

1 **P**lace the shaper on a sheet of centimeter grid paper. Hold the shaper so that no right angles are formed and the top and bottom edges align with the horizontal lines on the grid. Trace the outline of the shaper.

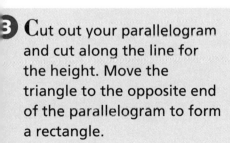

2 **T**he figure you created in Step 1 is called a **parallelogram.** Notice that each pair of opposite sides is parallel and has the same length. One of its sides may be identified as its **base.** The distance from the base to the opposite side is called the **height.** Draw a line on your parallelogram to represent the height as shown at the left.

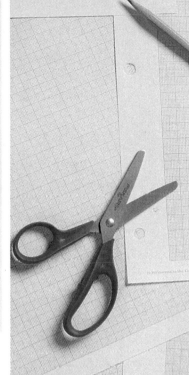

3 **C**ut out your parallelogram and cut along the line for the height. Move the triangle to the opposite end of the parallelogram to form a rectangle.

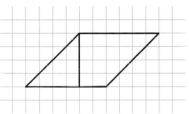

4 **R**epeat this process for several different parallelograms.

5 **W**rite a concluding statement explaining how the area of a parallelogram is related to the area of a rectangle.

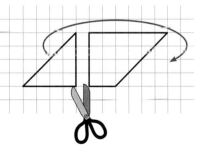

Twice the Fence!

The following advertisement was submitted to a local newspaper:

The WRAP IT UP! Fence Company
. . . is offering a once-in-a-lifetime opportunity!

Thinking about fencing in your yard?

Well, if you will just pay for twice the amount of fence you had intended to buy, we will guarantee to enclose an area that is *four times* as large as the original space.

Imagine that — *four times as large!*

Act now! This offer will not last.

Stop by our office today and make arrangements to get the fencing deal of a lifetime!

As advertising editor of the newspaper, you must determine whether the claim is true. You work for a very respectable newspaper that does not want to be associated with companies that are trying to swindle their customers. Your editor-in-chief has asked you to research this claim and submit your findings to her before running the advertisement. The Wrap It Up! Fence Company wants to run a full page advertisement everyday for a week.

Research the problem and design an argument that either supports or does not support running the advertisement.

1. Using centimeter grid paper, outline a square. Label the square A.
   - What is the perimeter of square A?
   - What is the area of square A?

   Draw a second square with sides that are twice as long as square A's. Label square B.
   - What is the perimeter of square B?
   - What is the area of square B?

   You can compare the length of a side of square A to the length of a side of square B using a **ratio**. A ratio is a comparison of two numbers by division. A common way to express ratios is as a fraction in simplest form.

   Write ratios comparing the length of the sides, perimeter, and area of square B to square A.

2. Draw a square that is larger than square A and smaller than square B. Label the square C.
   - What is the perimeter of square C?
   - What is the area of square C?

   Write ratios comparing the length of the sides, perimeter, and area of square C to square A.

3. Draw a square so that its length and width are three times as long as square C's. Label this square D.
   - What is the perimeter of square D?
   - What is the area of square D?

   Write ratios comparing the length of the sides, perimeter, and area of square D to square C.

4. Do you think that the results in parts 1, 2, and 3 would be the same if you started with a rectangle? Justify your response using mathematical reasoning.

5. Draw conclusions based on your explorations. Verify your conclusions by using two different size squares and two different size rectangles.

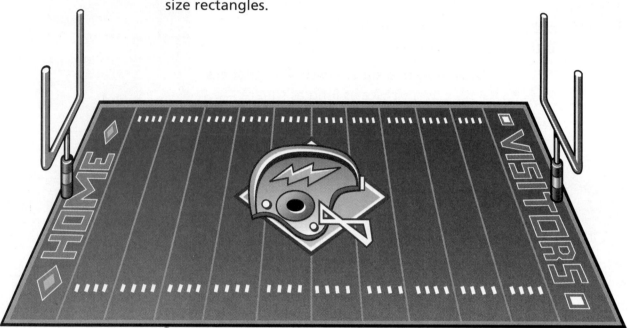

After verifying your conclusions, write a summary that explains what you have discovered. Be sure that your summary answers the following questions.

- Given a square, how will doubling the length of its sides affect the area?
- Given a square, how will increasing the length of its sides by adding an amount that is not a multiple of the original length increase the area?
- Given a rectangle, how will doubling its dimensions affect the area? How will tripling its dimensions affect the area?
- Will this be true of any two quadrilaterals? Of any two polygons?

WHAT'S THE CHANCE?

J.R. has just learned that part of her ranch covers an oil field.

The geologist who told her the possible location of the oil field gave a rather puzzling response to her questions about its location. What follows is a summary of the geologist's report.

> The boundaries of your land form a rectangle 2.4 miles wide and 6 miles long. One-half of your land contains no oil at all. The land that does have oil under it is in the shape of a triangle. This triangle is 1.6 miles deep, and the base is 1.9 miles long.

The land that has oil under it has no buildings on it so J.R. could drill anywhere on it. She would like to start drilling for the oil but doesn't know if she should take the chance. It is very costly to drill for oil so J.R. has hired you to research this opportunity and determine the chance of striking oil on the first attempt.

The **event,** or specific outcome, you are interested in is J.R. striking oil. **Probability** is the chance that an event will happen. The probability of an event is the ratio of the number of ways an event can happen to the number of possible outcomes. In this case, the probability that J.R. will strike oil is expressed by the fraction $\frac{\text{area of the oil field}}{\text{area of land containing the oil field}}$.

The probability that an event will happen is written as a number from 0 to 1. A probability of 0 means that the event is impossible. A probability of 1 means that the event is certain to happen. The closer a probability is to 1, the more likely the event is to happen.

- Prepare a recommendation for J.R. Use mathematical tools and reasoning to support your recommendation. Be prepared to defend your recommendation to the class.

Geology Report

Write a full page narrative on how you worked on this activity. Consider the questions below in writing your narrative. Use them to get started but don't simply write an answer to each question or limit yourself to answering only these questions. The narrative will be discussed as a class.

- Was it necessary to know how many acres J.R. owned in order to draw the map needed for this problem? Why or why not?
- Do you think that the map that you used was a good way to help you solve the problem? What other approaches might you have used instead?
- Is J.R. taking a chance if she drills for oil? Why or why not?
- If J.R. drills, what's the chance that she will strike oil?
- Would you do anything differently if you could do this activity over again? If so, explain what and why.

Trail Blazing

Mathematical Explorations is a company that specializes in blazing math trails through schools and school yards across America. Students are led through a series of activity locations that they follow in and around their school. Participants are asked to make conjectures about known shapes including perimeter and area. Stops on the trail can also include questions involving calculations from known or estimated values. Students may also be asked to make their own shapes using string or other items.

Mathematical Explorations would like to set up a math trail in your school. They would like the trail to include between twelve and fifteen activity locations that involve the use of perimeter, area, similar shapes, ratios, and probability. As a team, you are to design a math trail to be submitted to Mathematical Explorations. As you work, remember to try to use items that are already in existence combined with those that you could create or generate. Be creative!!

As a group, lay out the plans for a math trail in and around your school. Utilize items that you see everyday. You may use a 6-foot piece of string to help get measurements and dimensions of shapes and figures. Make some initial investigations and formulate a plan. Then, return to the classroom to work on the details. The structure of the trail should naturally lead participants from one site to the next (turning to your right and walking about 50 paces you will see...).

Be prepared to set up your trail and have your classmates participate in your trail. Remember, Mathematical Explorations is in need of a good math trail in your school!

The Bigger, the Better?

Governors in the United States are always bragging that their state is the biggest or the best. Many times they use statistics that can appear convincing, but are actually very misleading. For instance,

> "We have the most shoreline."
> "We have the largest population."
> "We have the most lakes."
> "We have the highest mountain."
> "We are the biggest."

As the owner of a public relations firm that has been hired by the state's bureau of travel and tourism, you need to clarify what is meant by biggest. Does it mean land area, perimeter around the state, or population? Does it make a difference? Does the state with the largest area also have the largest perimeter? Does the state with the largest population have the greatest area?

- Look at the states listed below and find them on a map. Use your map, string, grid paper, and the U.S. Facts sheets in the Data Bank to determine which of the states listed are the five biggest states. Rank them according to area, perimeter, and population. Does there seem to be a correlation?

Alabama	Florida	New York
Arizona	Kansas	North Carolina
Colorado	Massachusetts	Tennessee
Connecticut	Montana	Utah

- After your firm has conducted a thorough investigation, your task as the owner is to present your findings to the governor in the form of a report.

SELECTION AND REFLECTION

Think of an everyday example in which you could use area and perimeter (for example, framing a picture or installing a hidden fence to keep your dog in your yard).

How would the skills you've learned in this unit help you to accomplish your task?

How would they help you if you decided to change your original dimensions?

Think of at least two alternatives to your original dimensions.

Use drawings and diagrams to illustrate your responses. Write your response on a separate piece of paper.

Bored Stiff

The Problem

Irene Eckert, an eccentric millionaire, is so bored that she decides to withdraw one million one-dollar bills from the bank and stack them in a single column in her living room. Assuming each dollar bill is as thick as a page in this book, how tall will the stack be? Will it fit in her living room?

The Problem

Lawrence city code requires a party house to provide 9 square feet for each person on a dance floor. To have a square dance floor that is large enough for 50 people, how long should each side be? Round your answer to the nearest foot.

What a Card!

The Problem

Andre designs his own greeting cards. He begins with a square sheet of paper and folds it into a card that has a perimeter of 32 inches. How many square feet of paper will he need to buy in order to make 10 cards? Round your answer to the greatest square foot.

The Problem

Find at least five different objects around your house that have a circular base. Trace the base onto a piece of centimeter grid paper. Estimate the area of each circle by counting the squares within the circle drawn. Complete the chart below.

Let's define our relationship!

Object	Area	Circumference	Radius

What is the relationship between the radius and the area of a circle?

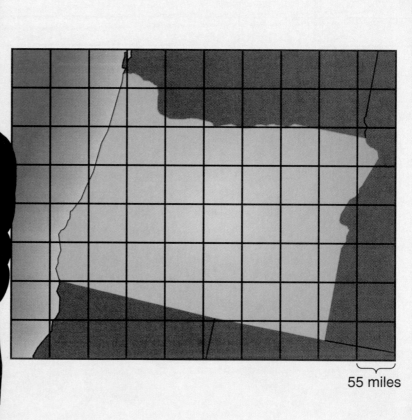

Geography Connection

N
W E
S

The Problem

Lisa Spyker works for the Oregon Department of Tourism and Travel. She travels to different parts of the country to promote tourism in her state. Right before doing a presentation, she realizes that she has forgotten her fact sheet that includes information such as the size of her state. She decides to use a map to estimate the size of Oregon. Use the map below to estimate the area of Oregon.

55 miles

The Problem

The groundskeeper for Candlestick Park in San Francisco is considering putting artificial turf on the football field in place of grass. He is not sure if the players will approve, so he decides to place artificial turf in a small area of the field as a test. He asks the artificial turf company to install an area of turf that is 10 yards by 20 yards, and he pays them $500.

After trying out the new turf, the athletes comment that there is not enough artificial turf to actually be able to determine if they like it. The groundskeeper calls the turf company again and asks them to double his original dimensions to 20 yards by 40 yards. He sends another check for $500.

The manager of the artificial turf company calls the grounds keeper back and says he still owes him $1,000. The groundskeeper is extremely confused and angry.

You have been hired by the artificial turf company to call on the groundskeeper to explain to him why he still owes $1,000. Prepare a presentation that you could use with the groundskeeper.

Just turf it out!

The Problem

Michael is taking golf lessons. He tees off and the ball lands in the rectangular region below.

- What is the probability that the ball lands on the green?

- What is the probability that the ball does not land in the sand trap?

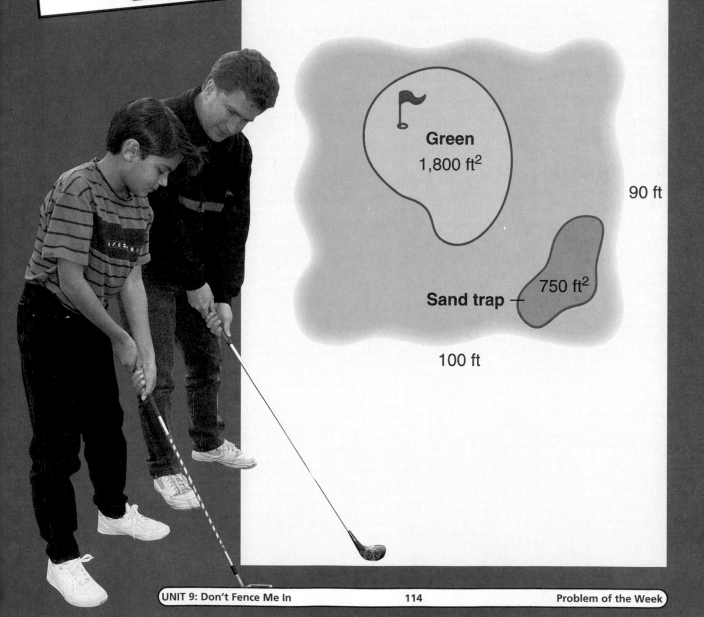

Green
1,800 ft^2

90 ft

Sand trap — 750 ft^2

100 ft

AGAINST THE ODDS

Looking Ahead

In this unit, you will see how mathematics can be used in determining fairness and probability. You will experience:

▶ solving problems involving probability and fairness

▶ determining probability ratios and probability values

▶ designing random-generating spinners

▶ designing games to meet certain specifications

▶ exploring odds, probability, and actual outcome

Did You Ever Wonder?

What do mathematics and the game of golf have to do with each other? Turn the page and see how Tiger Woods of Cypress, California, combines the two.

Teens in the News

Featuring: Tiger Woods
Age: 17
Hometown: Cypress, California
Career Goal: Professional Golfer
Interests: Conducting Golf
Clinics

If there is such a thing as a born golfer, Tiger Woods is one. He has been "playing" golf since he was 9 months old! At 11 months, he began hitting golf balls into a net with a toy club. Now, at age 17, Tiger hopes to become a professional golfer!

Tiger has been taking lessons from golf pros since he was 4 years old. He has traveled to Michigan, New York, Ohio, Pennsylvania, and Texas to play in amateur tournaments. *Golf Week*

Magazine and *Golf Digest* have named Tiger amateur player of the year. He was the number-one-ranked Junior Player in the United States two years in a row!

Tiger says mathematics is a big part of the game of golf. Golf clubs vary by length, weight, shape, and size. He must consider variables like distance to the hole, wind speed, elevation of the hole, and the lie of the ball to know which club to use. Tiger does this type of calculation many

times during a game because the conditions on the golf course change with each shot.

Tiger's expertise has already paid off. He will attend college on a golf scholarship. Tiger wants to earn a degree in accounting. He has seen too many professionals lose their money as a result of poor business management.

Tiger wants to wisely manage the money that he earns as a professional golfer.

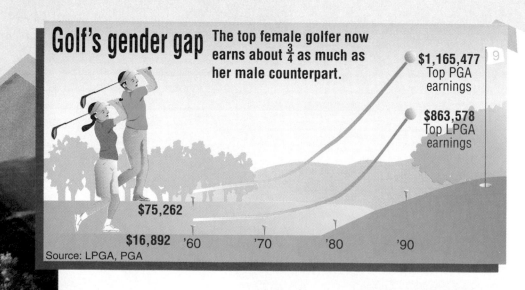

Golf's gender gap

The top female golfer now earns about $\frac{3}{4}$ as much as her male counterpart.

$1,165,477 Top PGA earnings

$863,578 Top LPGA earnings

$75,262

$16,892   '60   '70   '80   '90

Source: LPGA, PGA

Team Project

Your Best Shot

The best shot Tiger or any golfer can have is a hole-in-one. Research to discover the odds of getting a hole-in-one. Based on those odds, how many rounds of golf would you have to play to get one? Do you think the odds of a hole-in-one at miniature golf are better or worse than the odds of a hole-in-one at regular golf? Explain your answer.

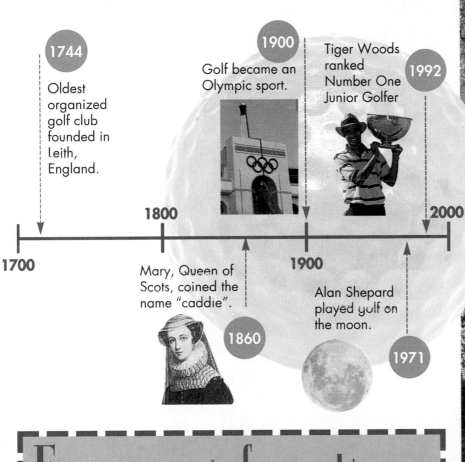

1744

Oldest organized golf club founded in Leith, England.

1900

Golf became an Olympic sport.

Tiger Woods ranked Number One Junior Golfer

1992

1800

1700

Mary, Queen of Scots, coined the name "caddie".

1860

1900

Alan Shepard played golf on the moon.

1971

2000

You can learn more about the math Tiger may use to determine his odds of winning a golf tournament by completing the activities in this unit.

For more information

If you would like more information about the game of golf, contact:

**UNITED STATES GOLF ASSOCIATION
BOX 708
Far Hills, New Jersey 07931**

Setting the Scene

MATHEMATICS TOOLKIT

Many professions require the use of tools. This mathematics toolkit includes tools you may find useful in this unit. At times you may feel lost and/or not know where to begin when presented with a problem situation. Take time to read this toolkit to see how the characters in the script used probability to solve their problem. You don't need to wait until your teacher tells you to make a chart or create a list. Instead, if it seems like it might help, try it.

Narrator: Emilio, Tom, and Yuji are friends. They are middle schoolers who love to play basketball.

Emilio: Hey, did you see the contest at the Shoelocker in the mall?

Tom: Yeah, it's all over the radio.

Emilio: You can win the Airborne-Rikees. They're $120 shoes!

Yuji: Yeah, those are great basketball shoes. They're worn by all the best basketball players.

Emilio: I know. And I'm going to win that contest!

Yuji: How are you going to pull that off?

Tom: Yeah, you know it's pure luck whoever wins.

Emilio: I've got a plan. You'll see.

Yuji: You've got to be kidding. You don't have a chance.

Emilio: Okay, but when I wear those Airborne-Rikees to our next game, don't be surprised!

Yuji: So, what's the big secret? Let's hear this plan.

Emilio: No way! You'll try to copy and blow my chances.

Yuji: We won't copy. Right, Tom?

Tom: Yeah, we promise. It probably won't work anyway...unless you cheat.

Emilio: I'm not going to cheat. I figured out how to do it mathematically.

Tom: So, tell us.

Emilio: Well, in Ms. Washington's math class, we're studying probability. We learned last week that if you have more entries in a contest than anyone else, then you have the best chance of winning.

Tom: So how are you going to get more entries than anyone else?

Emilio: Easy. The contest rules state that you can enter as many times as you like.

Yuji: Yeah, but it will cost you $2.00 per entry.

Emilio: Well, I've saved up $50 to buy those shoes. If I use that money in the contest, I can buy 25 tickets for that amount. That means my chances of winning are 25 times as great as the person who buys just one ticket. So I can get those Airborne-Rikees for just $50 and save $70 plus tax!

Tom: I don't know. Something doesn't sound right about that.

Emilio: Well, just ask your math teacher whether I have a good plan. But remember it's *my* plan. No copying...you promised!

Stop the Script!
Determine whether Emilio has a good plan. How could you determine his chances of winning? Would it be worth it?

Narrator: The students meet during lunch the next day. They start talking about the contest again.

Tom: So, Emilio, have you paid for your 25 contest entries yet?

Emilio: I'm going down to the mall after school today to ensure my victory.

Yuji: I think you should think about it more. I talked to my mom, and she said that it could backfire on you.

Emilio: Why is that? I bet you just don't want me to win. You're jealous that I thought of this plan first.

Yuji: No, it's not that. My mom said you don't know how many people are entering the contest and having 25 entries may not make a lot of difference if there are a lot of entries. Plus, someone could luck out and win with just one ticket.

Emilio: Yeah, but I still think having 25 tickets will give me a pretty good chance of winning.

Tom: Well, before you go and spend your money, my brother's friend works at the Shoelocker, and maybe I can find out how many entries there are. Why don't you wait until tomorrow?

Emilio: All right. But the contest closes tomorrow, so I can only wait one day.

Narrator: Tom talked with his brother's friend who works at the Shoelocker.

Emilio: What did your brother's friend tell you?

Tom: Well, he didn't know exactly, but he heard the store manager say that they have earned about $3,000 in the contest. That must mean they have about 1,500 entries.

Emilio: That's lots of entries...but is that good news or bad news?

Yuji: I know how to figure that out. We can find the probability of you winning by dividing the number of times you entered by the total number of entries.

If you buy 25 tickets, you will have 25 chances of winning. If there are 1,500 entries and you buy 25 tickets, there will be a total of 1,525 entries.

The probability of you winning, then, is $\frac{25}{1,525}$. If we divide that on a calculator, we get 0.01639.

Emilio: What does that mean? Is 0.01639 good or bad?

Tom: Well, it's not real good. The best probability is 1, or 100%. That would happen if you were the only one who entered the contest. The probability of you winning would be $\frac{25}{25}$, or 1.

The worst probability is 0. That would happen if you didn't enter at all. The probability of you winning would be $\frac{0}{1,500}$, or 0.

Emilio: So, you're saying probability is a number between 0 and 1.

Tom: Yes.

Yuji: And a 50-50 chance of winning would be a probability of 0.50.

Emilio: Hmmm. My probability is less than 0.02. That looks real bad. I don't want to throw my money away. Maybe I should go ask Ms. Washington what to do.

Narrator: Emilio goes to see his math teacher, Ms. Washington, and explains the situation to her.

Ms. Washington: Well, Emilio, I don't want to tell you how to spend your money, but I will show you how people use mathematics to help them make decisions regarding chance.

Emilio: Okay, maybe that will help me make up my mind.

Ms. Washington: What I'm going to show you is called **expected value**. Expected value helps us to determine what is most likely to happen.

You and your friends have already done most of the work. You have calculated that your probability is 0.01639. That means you will win a little less than 2% of the time.

Emilio: Let's just round off and use 2% then.

Ms. Washington: Okay. So tell me, what's your chance of losing?

Emilio: The total of either winning or losing is 100%. So, 100% − 2% = 98%. My chances of losing are 98%. Boy, that's pretty bad.

Ms. Washington: Yes. But remember, there's still the possibility that you could win $120 shoes for just $50.

Emilio: So how do price and cost work into this problem?

Ms. Washington: Well, that's where expected value comes in. First, you need to determine your expected value of *winning*. That is 2% times the amount you win, $120. That equals $2.40.

Next, you need to determine the expected value of *losing*. That is 98% times the $50 you would pay. That equals $49.

When you compare these two amounts, you find that on the average you will lose $49.00 − $2.40, or $46.60, every time you enter a contest using your plan of buying 25 tickets.

Emilio: Boy, I almost threw away my hard-earned money!

Ms. Washington: It's true that a person can be lucky, and of course, someone *will* win the contest, but you need to be careful about how much you risk because the odds are against you.

Emilio: I'm going to tell my friends that they saved me from losing all my money. But, I think I might go to the mall and enter once. You never know, I might be lucky!

This concludes the Mathematics Toolkit. It included many mathematical tools for you to use throughout this unit. As you work through this unit, you should use these tools to help you solve problems. You may want to explain how to use these mathematical tools in your journal. Or you may want to create a toolkit notebook to add mathematical tools you discover throughout this unit.

WHAT'S FAIR ABOUT THIS?

You work for a game manufacturer and it's your job to determine whether a certain new board game is fair or unfair. The game involves a track meet in which four racers (four players) each trying to make it to the finish line first.

Racer	Numbers
Racer A	3 or 4
Racer B	5 or 6
Racer C	7 or 8
Racer D	9 or 10
All racers move two spaces on 2, 11, or 12.	

To play, roll a pair of number cubes and add the numbers on the number cubes. The sum of the number cubes will match one of the racer's numbers in the table above. That racer moves three spaces and all the other racers move only one space. If the sum of the number cubes is 2, 11, or 12, then all players move two spaces. Take turns rolling the number cubes until one player reaches the finish line. The racer to reach the finish line first wins the race.

Play the game several times and record which racer wins each time. Determine whether the game is fair or unfair. Use the poster board or blank transparency provided by your teacher to write a report of your findings.

Game Fair
Quick on the Draw

This game is for two players. Select who will be Player A and Player B.

Each player places his or her tile at the starting line. Shuffle the deck of cards. One player draws a card. If a face card is drawn, Player A moves his or her tile two spaces on the game board. If an ace or a number card is drawn, Player B moves his or her tile one space on the game board.

Players alternate drawing a card until one player's tile reaches the finish line. That player wins the game.

MENU station B Number Cubes

This game is for two players. Select who will be Player A and Player B.

Each player places his or her tile at the starting line. One player rolls the number cubes. If the sum of the number cubes is an even number, Player A moves his or her tile one space on the game board. If the sum of the number cubes is an odd number, Player B moves his or her tile one space on the game board.

Players alternate rolling the number cubes until one player's tile reaches the finish line. That player wins the game.

Coin Toss

This game is for three players. Select who will be Player A, Player B, and Player C.

Each player places his or her tile at the starting line. One player tosses the coins. If the coins are both heads, Player A moves his or her tile one space on the game board. If the coins are a head and a tail, Player B moves his or her tile one space. If the coins are both tails, then player C moves his or her tile one space.

Players alternate tossing the coins until one player's tile reaches the finish line. That player wins the game.

FLIP THE CHIPS

This game is for two players. Select who will be Player A and Player B.

   Each player places his or her tile at the starting line. One player flips the chips. If the chips are both red, Player A moves his or her tile one space on the game board. If the chips are red and yellow, Player B moves his or her tile one space on the game board.

   Players alternate flipping the chips until one player's tile reaches the finish line. That player wins the game.

MENU
station
E

Don't Lose Your Marbles

This game is for three players. Select who will be Player A, Player B, and Player C.

Each player places his or her tile at the starting line. One player picks a marble from the bag. If the marble is red, Player A moves his or her tile one space on the game board. If the marble is yellow, Player B moves his or her tile one space. If the marble is blue, then Player C moves his or her tile one space. The marble is returned to the bag.

Players alternate picking a marble and returning it to the bag until one player's tile reaches the finish line. That player wins the game.

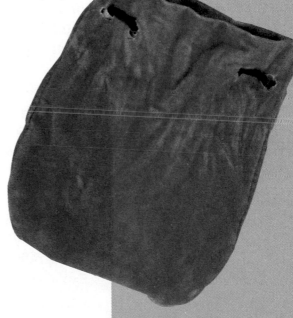

Probable Cause
What if....

- You took a survey of 50 adults and found that 15 of them smoke. If you were to randomly select one of the 50 people to interview, what is the probability that the person you select is a *nonsmoker*? Explain how you determined your answer.

- You put three blue marbles, four red marbles, and seven yellow marbles into a bag and shake the bag. You ask your friend to select a marble from the bag without looking. What is the probability that your friend selects a yellow marble? Explain how you determined your answer.

- You have a standard deck of playing cards. After shuffling the deck of cards, you pick one card. What is the probability that the card you pick is *not* an ace or a face card? Explain how you determined your answer.

- You roll three number cubes. What is the probability that the sum of the numbers on the number cubes is 15, 16, 17, or 18? Explain how you determined your answer.

- You have two chips. One chip is red on both sides, the other chip is red on one side and yellow on the other side. You put the chips in a cup, shake the cup, and spill the chips onto the table. What is the probability that at least one chip will show red? Explain how you determined your answer.

It Happened by Chance

Pick a card from the deck of fraction cards provided by your teacher. The fraction on the card represents a probability.

Think about situations in which events happen by chance. Write a paragraph describing a situation that involves the probability on the card you picked. Include any illustrations you may need to describe your situation. You can write your paragraph as a story if you would like.

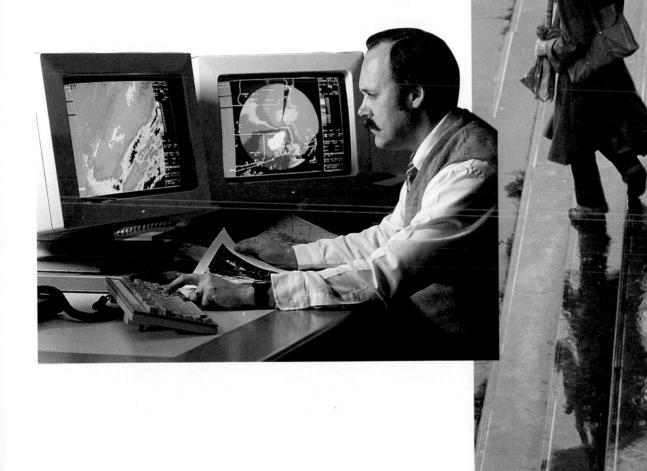

THE BIG SPIN
Round and Round it Goes....

Your teacher will provide your group with a set of clue cards. Each member of your group should select one clue card and hold onto it throughout the activity. You may not hand your card to anyone else. However, you may read it to your group members as many times as necessary.

As a group, use the clues on the cards to design a random-generating spinner. Once you have designed your spinner, use the clue cards to verify that you built a spinner that satisfies all the clues.

When your group has completed designing the spinner and verified its accuracy, each student should draw a model of the spinner to scale using a compass, protractor, pencil, and paper. Refer to the group card entitled *How to Build a Spinner* if you need help. Label each section of the spinner with the number of that section and its probability. Describe in writing the process your group used in designing the spinner and how you know it is accurate.

When your group has completed the first spinner, exchange clue cards with another group and repeat these instructions for a new spinner. You will continue to design spinners and exchange clue cards until you have five different spinners.

How to Build a Spinner

Cut a blank piece of paper into a square. Using a compass, draw a circle in the square. Mark the center of the circle with a dot.

To make a spinner you need to divide the circle into fractional parts called **sectors**. A sector of a circle is shaped like a piece of pie. Since there are 360 degrees (360°) in a circle, multiply each fraction by 360 to find the number of degrees in each sector of the spinner.

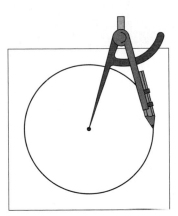

Example

Suppose you want a sector of a spinner to be $\frac{1}{3}$ of a circle.

To find out how many degrees this would be, multiply 360° by $\frac{1}{3}$. The central angle of the sector is 120°.

To draw a sector of 120°, draw a vertical line from the center of the circle to a point on the circle. This is a **radius** of the circle. Place a protractor on this radius with its center at the center of the circle. There are two scales on the protractor. Use the one that begins with 0° where the radius aligns with the protractor. Follow the scale from the 0° point to the 120° point. Make a small mark at this point and draw a line from the center of the circle through this point to a point on the circle. This is another radius of the circle.

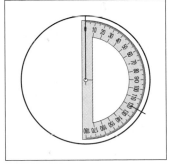

One way to make this sectored circle into a spinner is to place a pencil with a paper clip or bobby pin on its tip at the center of the circle and to spin the paper clip or bobby pin using your free hand.

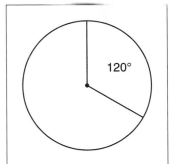

120°

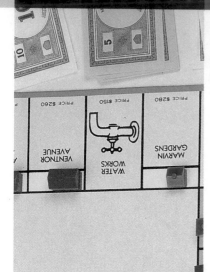

Play to Win

You are a game designer. Your boss has challenged you to design a game where one player has a definite advantage over the other player(s). She feels the company can market the game to people who are poor sports and always want to win.

The game needs to be designed in such a way that it is not obvious to the other player(s) that one player has an advantage. Your game may be a board game, a card game, or any other type of game. You can use any random-generating device you want. Your game may be designed so that the same player wins most of the time or all of the time. The game with the best design is the game in which the other players don't catch on too early that it is unfair.

Once you have come up with your design, write down the rules to the game. Include a special section on how the winning player has the advantage. Explain in those remarks the probability of that player winning the game and how you determined that value.

Share your game with others in the class. After playing the game a few times, have your challengers try to determine your winning strategy and the probability of you winning. Then switch roles, having one of your challengers become the player with the advantage. In these roles, do you get the same outcome?

After examining one designer's game, switch games and test a new game following the same procedure.

Odds and Ends
Spinning Out of Control

This game is for three players. Use the spinner and score cards provided by your teacher. Each player chooses a color: red, blue or green.

One player spins the spinner. If the spinner comes up red, then the red player places a tally mark in the win (W) column, and the blue and green players each place a tally mark in the loss (L) column. If the spinner comes up blue or green, the player whose color comes up tallies a win, and the other two tally a loss.

Spin the spinner 50 times. Write a ratio comparing your wins to your losses. This is your odds of winning the game. Using all three players' results, determine the probability of getting red, green, or blue on a single spin.

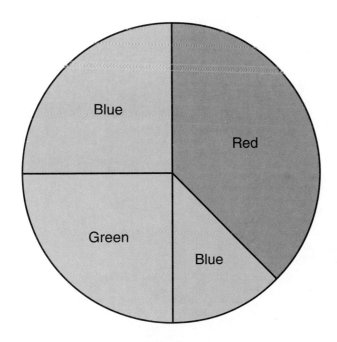

Some Sums

Tis game is for three players. Use the two number cubes, three different-colored tiles, and game board provided by your teacher. Players move their tile on the game board according to the following rules.

- Player A moves one space when a sum of 1, 2, 3, or 4 occurs.
- Player B moves one space when a sum of 5, 6, 7, or 8 occurs.
- Player C moves one space when a sum of 9, 10, 11, or 12 occurs.

Begin with three tiles at the starting line of the game board. Have one player roll the number cubes. Find the sum of the numbers on the two number cubes and move the appropriate tile one space on the game board. The first player to have his or her tile reach the finish line wins.

Play the game 12 times. Each player should keep track of the number of games won and the number of games lost.

Determine the odds of each player winning. Then determine the probability of each player winning. Describe in writing how the odds are related to the probability.

HOW THE CHIPS FALL

This game is for three players. Use the three two-colored chips, cup, three different-colored tiles, and game board provided by your teacher. Players move their tiles according to the following rules.

- Player A moves one space when the chips show exactly two red sides.

- Player B moves one space when the chips show *at least* two yellow sides.

- Player C moves one space when the chips are all the same color.

Begin with three tiles at the starting line. One player shakes the chips in the cup and pours them out. Based on how the chips fall, move the tile of Player A, B, or C one space on the game board. Notice that there are cases when two tiles may move on the same turn. The first player to have his or her tile reach the finish line wins.

Play 16 games. Each player should keep track of the number of games won and the number of games lost. Determine the odds of each player winning. Find the theoretical odds and compare to your experimental odds. Describe this comparison in writing.

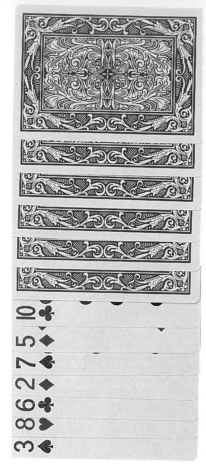

Stack the Deck

This game is for three players. Use the deck of cards, game board, and three different-colored tiles provided by your teacher. Players move their tiles according to the following rules.

- Player A moves one space when a face card is drawn.
- Player B moves one space when a red card is drawn.
- Player C moves one space when an even number (not a face card) is drawn.

One player draws a card. Depending on what card is drawn, Player A, B, or C moves his or her tile one space on the game board. Notice that there are cases when two tiles may move on the same turn. The first player to have his or her tile reach the finish line wins.

Play 20 games. Each player should keep track of the number of games won and the number of games lost. Determine the odds of each player winning. Find the theoretical odds and compare to your experimental odds. Describe this comparison in writing.

Name That Game

Design a spinner that produces a game situation having the following odds.

- Player A: 1 to 2
- Player B: 1 to 5
- Player C: 5 to 7
- Player D: 1 to 11

Play the game several times. Compare your actual outcomes to the odds stated above. Determine the probability of each player winning the game. Write about your findings.

SPINNER WINNER

An Odd Situation

Describe a situation outside of school that involves using odds. You may need to research a topic using newspapers or magazines. Write about the situation, list the odds given for that situation, and determine the probability of the situation occurring.

EVENING THE ODDS

Game 1

This game is for three players. It is played with two coins and a cup. The object of the game is for a player to get 25 points.

The number of points a player receives for a win is called a payoff value. The payoff values are as follows.

- Player A gets 2 points each time two heads occur.
- Player B gets 2 points each time two tails occur.
- Player C gets 1 point each time a head and a tail occur.

Players alternate shaking the coins in the cup and spilling them out on the table. Play this game several times and record your results. Is it a fair game for all the players? Justify your answer.

Game 2

This game is for two players. It is played with a deck of cards. The object of the game is for a player to get 50 points.

The payoff values are as follows.

- Player A gets 4 points each time an ace or face card is picked.
- Player B gets 2 points each time a numbered card is picked.

Shuffle the deck of cards and cut the deck. Players alternate picking the top card of the deck. Play this game several times and record your results. Is it a fair game for both players? Justify your answer.

Game 3

This game is for three players. It is played with two number cubes. The object of the game is for a player to get 50 points. The payoff values are as follows.

- Player A gets 5 points each time the sum of the number cubes is 7.
- Player B gets 2 points each time the sum of the number cubes is greater than 7.
- Player C gets 2 points each time the sum of the number cubes is less than 7.

Alternate rolling the number cubes. Play this game several times and record your results. Is it a fair game for all the players? Justify your answer.

Game 4

This game is for any number of players. It is played with a spinner. Using paper, a compass, and a protractor, make a spinner like the one shown below.

The object of this game is for a player to get 50 points. Points are awarded to the player according to his or her spin. Players alternate spinning the spinner and determining their points.

Play this game several times. Is it a fair game for all the players? Justify your answer.

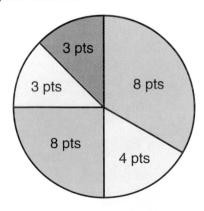

Game Time

Design your own game. Select a random-generating device and a game objective. Determine a payoff value for the occurrence of each possible event.

Determine whether or not your game is fair. If your game is fair, justify your conclusion. If your game gives certain players an advantage, determine how much of an advantage or disadvantage each player has.

Write about your game. Describe the process you used to determine whether the game is fair and who may have an advantage. Discuss why you believe you have accurately predicted whether the game is fair or not.

Share your game with a classmate or classmates (depending on how many are needed to play your game). Explain the rules to your classmate(s), and let them choose which players they prefer to be. Play your game several times to test your conclusions. Are your conclusions correct? Justify your answer.

COMPUTER
investigation

Chances Are

The computer program "Chances" allows you to "play" several rounds of a game in a short amount of time. Each round is called an **event**.

The computer asks you to input the number of players involved in each game. It then assigns a probability of winning and a payoff value to each player. Your task is to run three or four games and to determine if the games are fair or unfair for each player. The following instructions allow you to use the computer program "Chances."

1. Boot up the BASIC program.
2. Load the "Chances" program by typing: LOAD "CHANCES"
3. Run the program by typing: RUN
4. The program will ask the question:
   HOW MANY PLAYERS (2 TO 9)?
   Enter the number of players you wish to use in the game.

The program plays 25 events at a time. It reports back a summary of how many points each player gets for a win (the payoff value), how many wins each player has, how many points each player has, and the percent of the total points each player has.

Have the computer play as many events as you need to in order to determine whether the game is fair or unfair for each player.

Once you have arrived at your conclusions for the first game, try a different game. Determine whether this game is fair or unfair for each player. Repeat this process for at least one more game.

Record the results of all the games you played. Write a report summarizing your findings. Explain how you arrived at your conclusions and what process you used. Give specific examples to support your findings. Illustrate your findings with graphs, diagrams, or other pictorial representations of the data. Be prepared to discuss your report with the class.

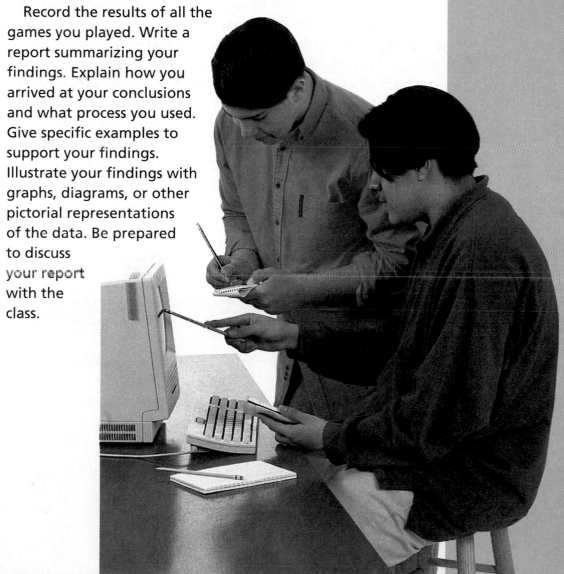

Board Games

Your group is part of Games Unlimited, Inc. Your assignment is to design a complex board game. Your game can be for two to six players and must include at least one random-generating device.

Select a theme for the game and create the graphic design of the game board on poster board. Develop instructions for the users of the game, complete with rules and objectives.

Due to a truth-in-advertising regulation, all game designers must explain the probability and odds of winning the game. They must also justify the fairness of the game to an inspecting agency. To satisfy this requirement, determine the probability and odds of winning your game and write a justification of the fairness of your game.

Plan and give an oral group presentation. Show your design to the class and give an explanation of the instructions. Demonstrate how to play the game. Give a detailed explanation of the probability and odds of winning the game and a justification of the fairness of the game.

What's Fair in Real Life?

Chance is a part of life. Whether you are playing a game, staying healthy, entering a contest, buying insurance, or trying to be safe, there is chance involved. In mathematics, we use probability to evaluate our chances. The probability of an event occurring enables individuals, companies, and government to make certain decisions. For example, an insurance company makes decisions about the cost of premiums based on the probability of certain accidents occurring. An individual may make a decision about using an exploratory medical drug based on the likelihood of it benefiting them rather than harming them. Knowing your chances enables you to make informed decisions.

This investigation allows you, as a student, to investigate a situation that involves chance and payoff values. You may use many sources to find a topic and data. Many of these sources are available in the library. A few suggested sources are periodicals, encyclopedias, medical journals, consumer catalogs, almanacs, sport statistics, electronic bulletin boards, or databases.

The data you choose could be the odds of winning the lottery, insurance tables, sport or game odds, disease or medical information, or social data. Some ideas for topics are listed below, but do not feel restricted to this list.

- What are the odds of winning the lottery? What is the expected value of buying one ticket? Is it worth the cost of playing?
- What is the probability of dying from smoking? What are the costs involved?
- What is the probability that a house in Southern California will be destroyed by an earthquake? Compare the cost of the insurance to the cost of rebuilding the home.
- What is the probability that a major-league baseball team will be a division winner if most of their games are played away?

- What is the probability of a player hitting a grand slam in the ninth inning of a World Series game?
- What is the probability of getting a false-positive on a drug test compared to the probability of finding someone who actually is a drug user?

Select a topic and write a statement describing the need to analyze the situation using the data.

Determine the data that will help you analyze the problem. Interview someone outside of school and ask this person what he or she might consider in analyzing the problem situation.

Analyze the data using the tools in this unit: probability, odds, expected value, and so on. Determine your findings and conclusions.

Write a detailed report, including the following information.
- a description of the topic to be analyzed
- a background statement regarding the topic
- a statement of the need or the problem to solve
- a rationale for choosing the topic
- the raw data used to analyze the situation and the source of the data
- an explanation of the analysis of the data
- a description of the probability tools used in analyzing the data
- an interview with someone outside of school on the analysis of the situation
- all conclusions and findings
- graphs or charts depicting the data and supporting your conclusions
- a summary of the process you used in completing this task

Selection and Reflection

In this unit, the mathematical terms *probability, fairness, odds, expected value,* and *payoff value* were often used.

What do these terms mean?

What do these words mean in terms of the work you did in this unit?

Describe what you know about each of these terms, using examples from the unit to help you describe and define them.

Fair Play... Or Not?

The Problem

Scott and his sister, Julie, are tired of playing the games they have at home, so they decide to make up a new game. They place four marbles in a bag. Two are red and two are blue. They take turns drawing two marbles from the bag. If the marbles are the same color, Scott gets a point. If the marbles are different colors, Julie gets a point.
After each draw the marbles are put back in the bag. Is this game fair or unfair? Explain.

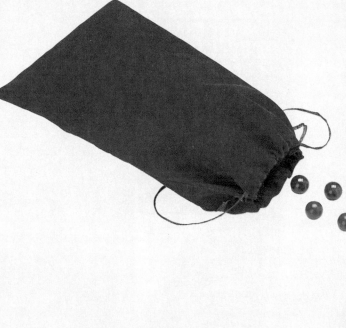

The Problem

Alfonso's dad takes Alfonso out to get a double dip of frozen yogurt for his birthday. The frozen yogurt shop offers a choice of six flavors: vanilla, chocolate, rocky road, strawberry, butter pecan, and mint chocolate chip. If Alfonso asks for two different flavors, what is the probability that he gets a scoop of chocolate and a scoop of mint chocolate chip? What is the probability that he gets this cone *and* the scoop of chocolate is on the bottom?

Color Me Pink

The Problem

Design a 4 × 4 checkerboard according to the clues listed below.

- The corner squares are all blue.
- The probability of dropping a pin and having its point land on a blue square is $\frac{3}{8}$.
- A blue square never touches another blue square on its side.
- A pink square never touches another pink square on its side.
- The probability of dropping a pin and having its point land on a pink square is $\frac{3}{8}$.
- All other squares are yellow.

Extension What is the probability of dropping a pin and having its point land on a yellow square?

The Problem

You and your friend have invented a new game called Crazy Cubes. To play the game, you roll two number cubes: one that has four sides numbered 1, 2, 3, and 4 and one that has six sides numbered 0, 1, 2, 3, 4, and 5. The object of the game is to roll both number cubes as many times as you want to get as close to, but not go over, a total score of 21. The person with the number of points closest to 21 is the winner. If you go over 21, you are disqualified and the other person automatically wins that round.

It is your turn. You have rolled the number cubes three times and your points add up to 18. Should you roll again to get closer to 21 or should you stop rolling and stay at 18 points? Explain your reasoning.

Crazy Cubes

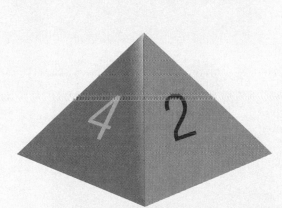

Are You A Leftie?

The Problem

The odds of having a left-handed child are 1 to 16 if neither parent is left-handed. If both parents are left-handed, the odds of having a left-handed child are *32 times as great*. What are the odds of two left-handed parents having a left-handed child? What is the probability of this occurring?

The Problem

The Hopi Indians invented a game of chance called Totolospi. This game was played with three cane dice, a counting board inscribed on stone, and a counter for each player. Each cane die can land round side up (R) or flat side up (F). In Totolospi for two players, each player places a counter on the nearest circle. The moves of the game are determined by tossing the three cane dice.

- Advance 2 lines with three round sides up (RRR).
- Advance 1 line with three flat sides up (FFF).
- Lose a turn with any other combination.

The player reaching the opposite side first wins.

If you are playing Totolospi with a friend, what is the probability that you will be able to advance your counter on the first toss?

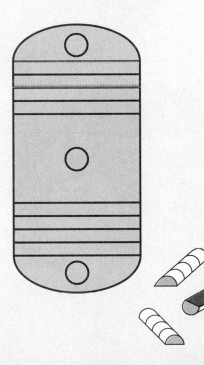

A Winning Combination

The Problem

The travel club at Girard Middle School has eight members. They raised enough money to pay for each member to go to Washington D.C., plus they had enough money left over to send three members to the state capitol for a weekend. They decide to have a drawing to determine who could go to the state capitol. Three names were chosen out of a hat. What is the probability that both you and your best friend in the club get to go on the trip?

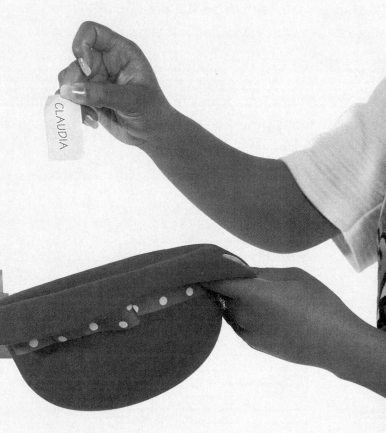

CYCLES

Looking Ahead

In this unit, you will see how mathematics can be used to answer questions about number patterns and operations. You will experience:

▶ solving problems involving time measurement

▶ exploring clock arithmetic

▶ solving problems using cyclical patterns

▶ using technology to collect data and solve problems

▶ converting between standard and base-ten time systems

Did You Ever Wonder?

What do mathematics and embroidery have to do with each other? Turn the page and see how Susan Behm of Westminster, Colorado, combines the two!

Teens in the News

Featuring: Susan E. Behm
Age: 19
Hometown: Westminster, Colorado
Career Goal: Business Management
Interests: Computers,
 playing the accordion

Some people just have a knack for computers. Susan E. Behm is one of those people. In her early teens, Susan took all the computer courses she could.

When Susan was 15, her mother was working for a company that makes embroidery machines. Her mother brought home a demonstration machine. Susan was fascinated by this sewing machine that was attached to a computer! Susan could type into the computer any size design and custom specifications she wanted on a shirt, sweater, or jacket. The computer would read her specs into a design program and then into the sewing machine.

Susan really got hooked on creating her own customized designs. Now her mother works for her, and they run **Suzie Q's Embroidery** out of the basement of their home!

Susan uses what she learned in geometry to help create her designs. She determines the size of the design and finds the exact center of it to place it on the material. She calculates the per-piece cost of each item as well as taxes.

Susan wants to expand her business. She plans to have a larger shop and hire full-time employees. She also intends to purchase her own digitizing machine. Then she could create and program her own designs onto computer disks. The next time you buy an item with customized lettering and designs, look for **Suzie Q's Embroidery** label.

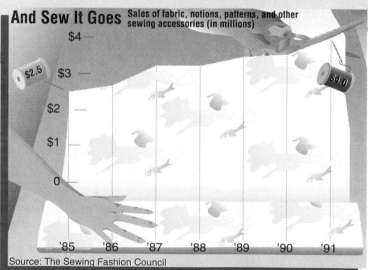

And Sew It Goes Sales of fabric, notions, patterns, and other sewing accessories (in millions)

$4 —
$2.5
$3 —
$2 —
$1 —
0
$4.0

'85 '86 '87 '88 '89 '90 '91

Source: The Sewing Fashion Council

Team Project

Designs in Time

Suzie Q's Embroidery has hired you to create a customized design. This design will appear on shirts, jackets, and sweaters. Your design should appeal to the students at your school.

The computers at Suzie Q's Embroidery read stitch commands in the form of ordered pairs. The machines can make stitches in multiples of $\frac{1}{16}$-inch lengths, from $\frac{1}{16}$ inch to 1 inch.

The machines can make 10 stitches per second.

Create your design and "program" the computer. How long will it take the machine to produce your design?

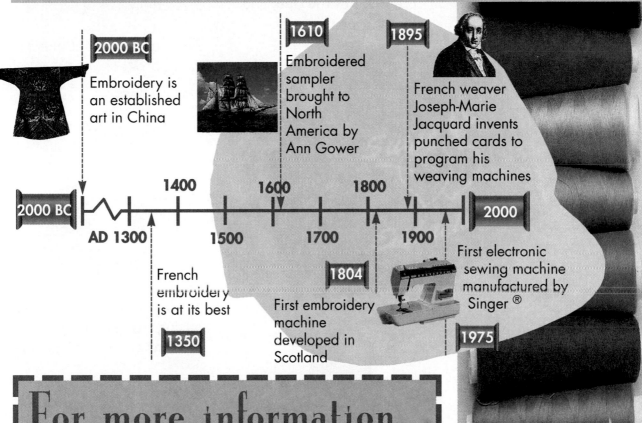

2000 BC — Embroidery is an established art in China

1350 — French embroidery is at its best

1610 — Embroidered sampler brought to North America by Ann Gower

1804 — First embroidery machine developed in Scotland

1895 — French weaver Joseph-Marie Jacquard invents punched cards to program his weaving machines

1975 — First electronic sewing machine manufactured by Singer ®

Timeline: 2000 BC, AD 1300, 1400, 1500, 1600, 1700, 1800, 1900, 2000

For more information

If you would like more information about forming your own company, contact:

JUNIOR ACHIEVEMENT, INC.
National Headquarters
One Education Way
Colorado Springs, Colorado
80906

You can learn more about the math Susan uses in her business by completing the following activities in this unit.

Setting the Scene

MATHEMATICS TOOLKIT

Many professions require the use of tools. This mathematics toolkit includes tools you may find useful as you study this unit. At times you may feel lost or not know where to begin when presented with a problem situation. Take time to read this toolkit to see the different mathematical tools and problem-solving strategies the characters in the script used. You don't need to wait until your teacher tells you to use a mathematical tool. Instead, if it seems like it might help, try it.

Narrator: Isabel, Teresa, John, Mario, Jason, and Lynn are officers in the Ecology Club at Lincoln Middle School. They are having a meeting in January. Isabel is the president of the club, and Jason is the treasurer.

Isabel: Now it's time for the treasurer's report. Jason, are you ready?

Jason: Well, sort of.

Lynn: What do you mean, "sort of"?

Jason: It means I kinda messed up.

Mario: Does that mean we're broke?

Jason: I don't know. I'm having trouble making sense of all these numbers.

John: Do you have the amounts we spent on the recycling bins for the school?

Teresa: How about the money we earned each week from collecting aluminum cans?

Jason: Yeah, yeah. I've kept good records. I'm just confused about what to do with all these numbers.

Isabel: We need to figure this out so we know how much we can spend for Arbor Day and Earth Week.

Mario: So far we have been spending money out of the student activities fund. We might really be broke.

John: I know. We'd better figure this out or we could be paying money out of our own pockets. They might not let us graduate.

Teresa: Don't panic. Jason has everything we have earned and spent listed here.

Narrator: Below is the list of all income (earnings) and expenditures (expenses) for this year.

John: Wow, look at this list! I can't tell whether we owe money or not.

Lynn: We need to figure it out quickly, so we know how much money we have.

Date	Transaction	Amount
9/10	Earnings from aluminum can weekly recycling	15.31
9/17	Earnings from aluminum can weekly recycling	12.78
9/21	Purchased 5 recycling bins for school	55.00
9/24	Earnings from aluminum can weekly recycling	17.56
10/1	Earnings from aluminum can weekly recycling	14.43
10/3	Purchased 3 recycling bins for school	33.00
10/8	Earnings from aluminum can weekly recycling	11.94
10/15	Earnings from aluminum can weekly recycling	13.89
10/17	Purchased 4 trees for community planting	26.40
10/22	Earnings from aluminum can weekly recycling	14.22
10/24	Purchased supplies for Halloween party	36.12
10/29	Earnings from aluminum can weekly recycling	15.92
11/5	Earnings from aluminum can weekly recycling	12.87
11/12	Earnings from aluminum can weekly recycling	14.66
11/15	Purchased 6 trees for community planting	39.60
11/19	Earnings from aluminum can weekly recycling	13.20
11/25	Earnings from aluminum can weekly recycling	8.17
12/2	Earnings from aluminum can weekly recycling	16.23
12/5	Purchased 7 recycling bins for school	77.00
12/9	Earnings from aluminum can weekly recycling	14.94
12/16	Earnings from aluminum can weekly recycling	13.33
12/20	Purchased supplies for holiday party	68.45
12/23	Earnings from aluminum can weekly recycling	12.74
1/14	Earnings from aluminum can weekly recycling	16.23

Isabel: Remember, we planned to spend $40 to buy three more trees for Arbor Day and about $100 for Earth Week.

Mario: Yeah, and we were also hoping to buy another six recycling bins for the areas we don't have covered on campus.

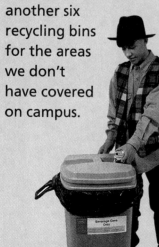

Teresa: I think we will have enough for all of those things. Remember we collect aluminum cans and turn them in each week for cash. School doesn't let out until the second week in June.

Lynn: The worst case is that we will have to hold another fundraiser so that we don't go bankrupt!

John: Let's stop talking and start figuring this out right now.

Stop the Script!
Determine the Ecology Club's account balance. Also, determine a budget for the remainder of the school year. Be prepared to share your budget with the rest of the class.

Narrator: The six officers start figuring out the account balance.

Mario: I know an easy way to figure out our balance using rational numbers and a calculator.

John: Rational numbers?

Mario: You know, fractions, decimals and signed numbers. You use + and −.

Lynn: That's right. Use a + sign for the money we earn and a − sign for the amount we spend.

Teresa: So our list would look like this?

Narrator: Teresa shows the group the list at the right.

Mario: Yeah, you got it. Just put a + in front of the amounts we earned and a − in front of the amounts we spent.

Date	Transaction	Amount
9/10	Earnings from aluminum can weekly recycling	+ 15.31
9/17	Earnings from aluminum can weekly recycling	+ 12.78
9/21	Purchased 5 recycling bins for school	− 55.00
9/24	Earnings from aluminum can weekly recycling	+ 17.56
10/1	Earnings from aluminum can weekly recycling	+ 14.43
10/3	Purchased 3 recycling bins for school	− 33.00
10/8	Earnings from aluminum can weekly recycling	+ 11.94
10/15	Earnings from aluminum can weekly recycling	13.89
10/17	Purchased 4 trees for community planting	6.40
10/22	Earnings from aluminum can weekly recycling	.22
10/24	Purchased supplies for Halloween party	.12
10/29	Earnings from aluminum can weekly recycling	
11/5	Earnings from aluminum can weekly recycling	
11/12	Earnings from aluminum can weekly recycling	
11/15	Purchased	for community planting	
11/19	Earn	can weekly recycling	3.2
11/25	Ear	can weekly recycling	
12/2	Ea	can weekly recycling	
12/5		bins for school	
12/9		num can weekly recycling	
12/16		weekly recycling	
12/20		oliday party	
12/23		m can weekly recycling	4
1/14		num can weekly recycling	.23

Jason: So how does that work with a calculator?

Lynn: Easy. First clear the calculator. Then press the key for the sign and type in the number. Then enter the next sign and the next number, over and over again until you get to the end of the list. At the end, you press 🔲.

John: So how does the calculator do it? I mean, what is the calculator actually doing?

Isabel: It's just adding up the numbers.

Jason: Adding? Don't those minus signs mean subtract and the plus signs mean add? How can you subtract a larger number from a smaller number?

Mario: When you combine rational numbers, you can think of it as adding and subtracting. Really it is just moving along a number line.

money you owe move left   **money you have move right**

$$-6 \quad -4 \quad -2 \quad 0 \quad 2 \quad 4 \quad 6$$

For example, suppose you have $5 and you want to buy something that costs $9. You start with 5 and move back nine (–9). That means you are $4 short.

money you owe   **money you have**

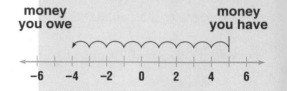

$$-6 \quad -4 \quad -2 \quad 0 \quad 2 \quad 4 \quad 6$$

Jason: So if you buy something for $10, then you make it a negative number, –10, and you move to the left 10 spaces on the number line?

Lynn: Yes, and if you start out owing somebody like your Mom $3, you start at –3. Suppose you get paid $7. Then you move to the right 7 spaces. You can pay your Mom back and have $4 left.

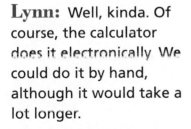

Teresa: So the calculator is moving along the number line?

Jason: What does that mean?

John: It means we're bankrupt!

Teresa: You panic too much. The student activities fund will cover us for now. We still have five more months of income from our recycling projects.

Mario: Yeah, we're almost $100 in the hole!

Jason: How much will that be?

Lynn: Well, kinda. Of course, the calculator does it electronically. We could do it by hand, although it would take a lot longer.

John: Hey, that's what technology is for! Isabel, just use the calculator.

Isabel: Okay, I just entered the last number and I'm pressing the equal sign, $\boxed{=}$. There, we get –97.15.

Isabel: Let's figure out what our average income is each week.

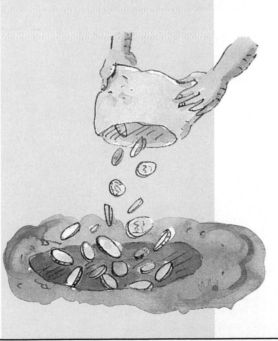

Lynn: Okay, I'll find the mean by adding up all the income and dividing by the number of weeks.

15.31 ⊞ 12.78 ⊞ 17.56 ⊞ 14.43 ⊞ 11.94 ⊞ 13.89 ⊞ 14.22 ⊞ 15.92 ⊞ 12.87 ⊞ 14.66 ⊞ 13.20 ⊞ 8.17 ⊞ 16.23 ⊞ 14.94 ⊞ 13.33 ⊞ 12.74 ⊞ 16.23 ⊟ *238.42*

Our total income is $238.42 and there were 17 weeks.

238.42 ⊡ 17 ⊟ *14.024706*

So, we make an average of about $14 per week.

John: How many weeks of school are left?

Jason: Here, I'll count them. There is a calendar on the wall. Not counting spring break, there are 19 more weeks of school.

Mario: Okay, 19 weeks times $14 per week makes $266. We owe $97.15. I'll combine −97.15 with +266.

⊟ 97.15 ⊞ 266 ⊟ *168.85*

We should have $168.85 by the time school is out for summer.

Isabel: So, we can use $168.85 for Arbor Day and Earth Week?

John: Can we buy any more recycling bins?

Teresa: We can't keep spending money that we don't have yet.

Lynn: We need to make a new budget before we can spend any more money. Jason, here, I'll show you how to set it up.

You make two different columns. One is for income (earnings) and one is for expenditures (expenses). First the income:

Narrator: Lynn shows the following list to Jason.

Lynn: Yes, that's right, but remember it is still an estimate. Now for the expenditures, we do a similar thing.

Narrator: Lynn creates the list at the right and shows it to Jason.

Expenditures	
Spend to date:	−335.57
Earth Day:	−100.00
Arbor Day:	−40.00
Total expenditures:	−475.57

Income	
Earned to date:	238.42
Estimated earnings:	266.00
Total income:	504.42

Jason: I get it. You have listed all the money we have earned so far from recycling and what we estimate we will make over the next five months. So, the $504.42 is what we will make over the entire year.

Jason: I see. The negative number –335.57 means we spent that amount so far this year. For Earth Week and Arbor Day we expect to spend those other amounts listed, –100.00 and –40.00.

John: And the –475.57 is the amount of money we expect to spend this year.

Lynn: Right. So now we find the balance by adding or combining those two totals. Using the calculator, we get our balance.

504.42 ⊟ 475.57 ⊟ *28.85*

John: Since the answer is positive, we won't be bankrupt!

Mario: I know. If the balance was negative we would owe the school money.

Teresa: I guess that means we can buy a couple of recycling bins.

Isabel: Not yet. Remember it's only an estimate. Maybe we should put some money in savings to be safe.

Jason: Good, I feel a lot better now about this budget.

John: We all should. I think we just lucked out. From now on we better keep up on this budget!

This concludes the Mathematics Toolkit. It included many mathematical tools for you to use throughout this unit. As you work through this unit, you should use these tools to help you solve problems. You may want to explain how to use these mathematical tools in your journal. Or you may want to create a toolkit notebook to add mathematical tools you discover throughout this unit.

The Ice Age

You work for InGen Corporation, a biotechnology company in the silicon valley near San Jose, California. You have been assigned to work in their pre-historic investigation division.

This division of InGen works with archaeologists who recover fossils. InGen uses various methods such as carbon-14 dating and bone-structure analysis of the fossils to determine the length of time since an animal died.

A Neanderthal fossil has been found in a cave in La Chapelle-aux Saints, France. The InGen lab has just finished the carbon-14 dating and the bone-structure analysis of the fossil. Your division has been asked to determine the date and time the Neanderthal died and the date the Neanderthal was born. (Use the modern calendar.)

Use the InGen Corporation lab report in the Data Bank to complete your assignment. Write a group report. Be prepared to share the methods you used to arrive at the dates.

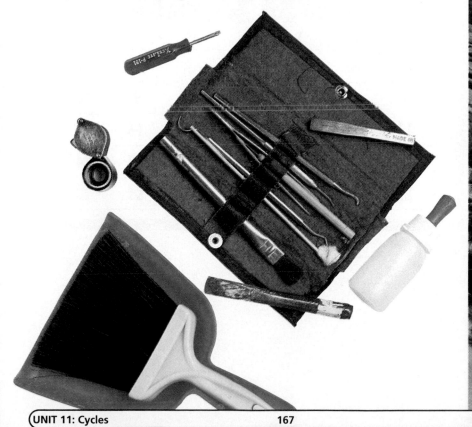

MENU station A

CALENDARS

If there are 365 days in a normal year, 366 days in a leap year (adding Feb. 29th to the calendar), and 7 days in a week, how many different calendars are there?

Two calendars are the same if every date of one calendar correspondingly falls on the same day of the week as the other calendar.

How many years pass before a calendar is repeated? Does it matter if the year you start with is leap year?

How many years does it take before each calendar is used once? Start counting with year 2001.

S	M	T	W	Th	F	S
■	■	■	■	1	2	3
4	5	6	7	8	9	10
11	12	13	14	15	16	17
18	19	20	21	22	23	24
25	26	27	28	29	■	■

► **FEBRUARY** ◄

How Long?

How long is 25 years, 12 weeks, 4 days, and 23 minutes?

State your answer in terms of seconds.

State your answer in terms of minutes.

State your answer in terms of days.

State your answer in terms of weeks.

MENU
station
C

How Old?

How old are you exactly?

In years?	In days?
In weeks?	In hours?
In minutes?	In seconds?
In seasons?	In months?
In decades?	In scores?
In centuries?	

What problems occur in determining the above information?

QUICK!
BLOW OUT YOUR
CANDLES!

Leaps

How many Februarys since 1600 have had five Sundays?
In what years of our modern calendar do New Year's Day
and New Year's Eve fall on the same day of the week?
Explain your answer.

MENU station E

Chime Times

A grandfather clock chimes 4 times when it is fifteen minutes after the hour, 8 times on the half-hour, 12 times when it is forty-five minutes after the hour, and on the hour it chimes 16 times plus it chimes the number of times equal to the hour. In one year, how many chimes are struck by the grandfather clock?

Game Clock

As a group, select one of the three game boards. Each pair should play the clock game several times. Record the sum of the number cubes for each move. Record the direction of each move by writing a positive sign (+) in front of the sum when you decide to go around the circle clockwise and a negative sign (−) in front of the sum when you decide to go around the circle counter-clockwise. In each game, you will create a list of signed whole numbers, or **integers**, to symbolize the size and direction of each move. You will use these lists later to analyze your moves.

After playing several games, determine who was able to finish a game in the fewest moves. How many moves? What was the greatest number of moves needed to finish a game? What is the average number of moves it took to finish a game in your group?

Once everyone in your group has played several games and discussed the results, try a different game circle. Play several games on that new circle as you did on the first. Did you find any difference between the two circle games?

Game Rules: The object of the game is to land on every numbered spot around the circle using as few moves as possible. Start at spot 0, but don't place a marker there. Roll three number cubes. The sum of the number cubes is the number of spaces you move. You may go around the circle in either direction (clockwise or counter-clockwise). Record the move. Move to the new location and place a marker there. If you have already visited that spot on the circle, move there but don't leave another marker. From the new location, repeat the process. The game ends when you have placed a marker on each spot on the circle.

Clock Five Game Board

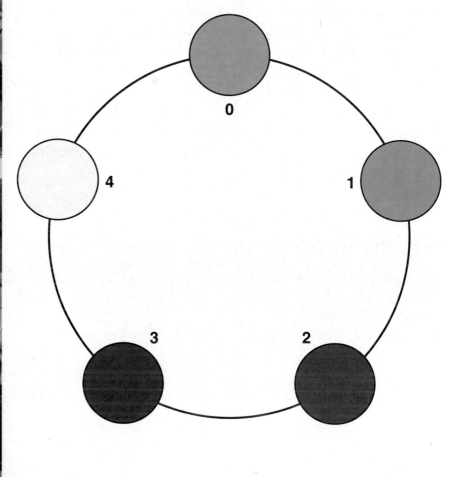

Exchange two or three circle game records with another pair. Replay the games they played. Determine if they could have finished the games in fewer moves by moving in the opposite direction on some of the turns.

Explain how you examined the games. If you found a faster method to finish a game, explain your method. If you think the other pair used the best strategy, show how the game could have been played to finish in more turns.

Select the records of the circle games you finished in both the most and least number of moves. Analyze those two games.

Longest game: Rearrange the order of the rolls to finish the game in the fewest number of moves. You cannot change the direction on a particular move; you can only change the order that the sums were rolled.

Shortest game: Rearrange the order of the rolls to finish the game in a different sequence. You cannot change the direction on a particular move; you can only change the order that the sums were rolled. Does the new game take more or fewer moves?

Explain how you analyzed the games. Did you find an easy method to solve these problems? What have you found out about the order of the rolls?

Back to theFuture

Solve these problems in your group. Then each member of the group should write a note to another student describing the method(s) used to solve these problems.

- What time was it 7 hours ago if it is 5 o'clock now?
- It is 9 o'clock. What time was it 6 hours ago?
- It is 8 o'clock. What time will it be in 12 hours?
- What time was it 5 hours ago if it is 5 o'clock now?
- Today is Thursday. What day will it be in 5,000 days?
- Today is Monday. What day was it 11,352 days ago?
- This month is October. What month will it be in 30 months?
- This month is March. What month was it 300 months ago?
- This month is October. What month will it be in 3,003 days?

Dividing Time

Marty said to Doc, "So, we are going to travel back in time. What year did you set the Delorean for?"

"Ohhh, I forgot," said Doc.

"What do you mean?" exclaimed Marty. "We could be lost in a time continuum!"

"Well, what I remember is... if you divide that year by 2," Doc said, "you'll get a remainder of 1."

"Great Doc, that's every odd-numbered year. You gotta remember more!"

"Great Scott! I just got a jolt of 1.21 gigabytes of brain power. Now I know. If you divide the year by 3, 4, 5, 6, 7, or 9, you'll also get a remainder of 1."

"What about 8? If I divide by 8, do I get a remainder of 1?" asked Marty.

"No, Marty," replied Doc.

Marty said, "Alright Doc, that's it! Let's go."

What year are they off to? Be prepared to present your solution. Be creative with your presentation.

Times Square

Consider a clock with seven digits as shown below. Multiplication in a clock system is repeated addition as in regular arithmetic. For example, 3 times 4 means to start at 0 and count to 4 three times while moving around the clock in a clockwise direction. The result is 5.

Create a multiplication table for clock seven. Examine the multiplication table that you have created. Describe the features of the table. Are there patterns that appear? Explain.

Create two more clock multiplication tables for two other clock sizes. What have you discovered about clock multiplication?

Create a multiplication table in clock twelve. Explain patterns you found in creating the table. How did you determine the answer to each multiplication problem?

X	0	1	2	3	4	5	6
0							
1							
2							
3							
4							
5							
6							

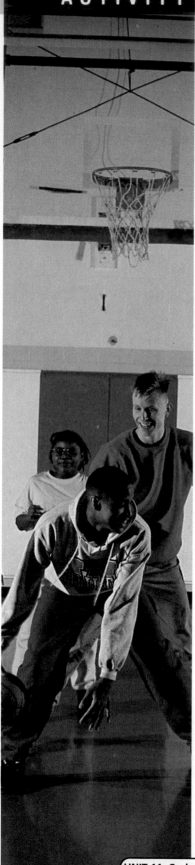

Team Schedule

You are the student representative on the facility planning committee for Hoover Middle School. You have both a gym and a cafeteria on your campus. The dance team, basketball team, and wrestling team can use either of these two facilities for their events.

From November 1 through March 30, these teams have scheduled events.

- The dance team has an event scheduled for Monday, November 1, and every <u>third school day</u> after November 1 (Thursday, November 4; Tuesday, November 9; and so on).
- The basketball team has its first home game on Tuesday, November 2, and every <u>fourth school day</u> after that (Monday, November 8; Friday, November 12; and so on).
- The wrestling team has its first home match on Wednesday, November 3, and every <u>fifth school day</u> after that (Wednesday, November 10; Wednesday, November 17; and so on).

The Hoover school calendar includes the following holidays.

Thanksgiving: Thursday, November 25–Friday, November 26
Winter break: Monday, December 20–Friday, December 31
Dr. Martin Luther King Day: Monday, January 17
Presidents' Day: Monday, February 21

If it is not a leap year, are there any dates when all three teams have events on the same day?

Prepare a report for the planning committee. If there are conflicting dates, state the dates, explain how you determined those dates, and how you know there are not any more conflicting dates. If there are no conflicting dates, explain how you know for sure, and how you arrived at your answer.

Eccentric Clockmaker

An eccentric clockmaker built three different clocks.

The first clock was a five-minute clock designed with an alarm set to sound each time the hand reached the number 2 on the clock.

The second clock was a six-minute clock designed to sound each time the hand reached the number 3.

The third clock was a seven-minute clock designed to sound each time the hand reached the number 4.

The clockmaker started the clocks simultaneously one day, and each clock began to sound at its appropriate time. Was there a time when all three clocks sounded their alarms together? If so, tell when it occurred and explain why. If not, explain why not.

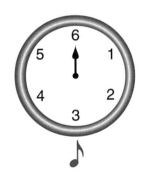

Spirolaterals

Spirolaterals are graphs made from sequences of numbers. The key to drawing any spirolateral is to follow this sequence of moves: UP-RIGHT-DOWN-LEFT. For example, to draw a 1, 2, 3 spirograph, first mark a starting point on graph paper. Next move up 1 space, then move right 2 spaces, and then move down 3 spaces. That completes one cycle. Continuing, you move left 1 space, move up 2 spaces, and move right 3 spaces.

A closed spirolateral is a spirolateral that will repeat itself after a number of cycles. In other words, after a certain number of cycles, a closed spirolateral will end in the same position and orientation where it originally began.

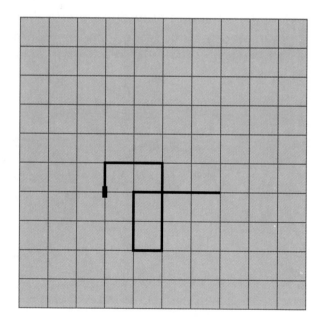

Using Graph Paper

A sequence with three terms forms an order—3 spirolaterals.

Draw a 4, 2, 1 and a 4, 3, 2 spirolateral.

Remember the key to drawing any spirolateral is UP-RIGHT-DOWN-LEFT.

On graph paper, draw an order-6 spirolateral like 4, 2, 6, 3, 7, 1. How does the sequence compare to an order-3 sequence? How does it differ?

On graph paper, draw other spirolaterals of your own. Record the sequence of numbers and describe each graph.

What are the characteristics of spirolaterals? Explain your findings.

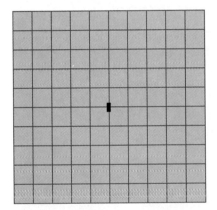
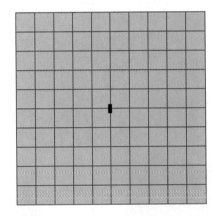

COMPUTER investigation

Using LOGO

Investigate spirolaterals using the computer. Type SPGRAPH 90 [1 2 3] in LOGO to draw a spirolateral with a sequence of 1,2,3. Make sure to type square brackets around the sequence of numbers and to separate the numbers in the sequence by *spaces*, not commas.

Your task is to discover properties of spirolaterals and to be able to generalize and predict the behavior of a spirolateral. Use the computer to draw and explore spirolaterals. Explain why you believe spirolaterals behave as they do.

Suppose the definition of a spirolateral is altered to allow the turning angle to change (for example, from 90° to 60°). How would that change the properties of closed spirolaterals? To explore these spirolaterals, substitute 60 for 90 in the program statement, i.e., SPGRAPH 60 [1 2 3]. Use isometric dot paper to draw a 60° spirolateral.

Write a report stating all the properties of spirolaterals that you have discovered during your investigations. Explain the process you used. Give specific examples to support your generalizations and draw diagrams to illustrate your findings.

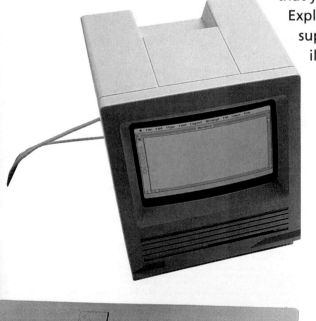

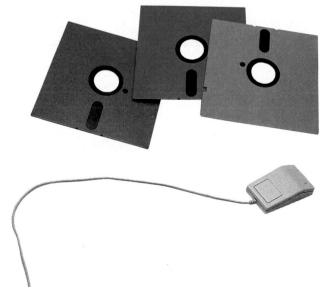

Metric Time

Suppose you invent a metric clock using the system below.

  1 day = 10 metric hours
  1 metric hour = 10 metric minutes
  1 metric minute = 10 metric seconds
  1 metric second = 10 metric miniseconds

If a standard and a metric clock are started together (the standard clock at 12:00 midnight and the metric clock at 0), what is the time in our standard system when the metric clock registers 4 metric hours, 5 metric minutes, 6 metric seconds, and 7 metric miniseconds?

Suppose a metric calendar uses the system below.

  1 day = 1 metric day
  1 metric week = 10 metric days
  1 metric month = 10 metric weeks
  1 metric year = 10 metric months

If both calendars begin at 0 B.C., what was the metric calendar date on January 1, 1993? Explain how you arrived at your solution.

Jurassic Time

You work for InGen Corporation, a biotechnology company in the silicon valley. You have been assigned to work in their pre-historic investigation division. The division works with archaeologists in the field who recover dinosaur fossils. InGen uses various methods of dating to determine the length of time since a dinosaur died.

Your division has been assigned the task of determining a process for calculating the hour, day, month, and year a dinosaur died, given the length of time its fossil has existed. Use the modern calendar. Your process should be clear and work for any number of different time lengths. Explain why your process works.

Use three time measurements to demonstrate the accuracy of your process.

Prepare a presentation of your process for the InGen Corporation.

Galactic Time

Linear, volume, temperature, and weight measurements have been converted from traditional measures to metric units. Standard units such as yards, miles, quarts, pounds, and degrees Fahrenheit have given way to meters, kilometers, liters, kilograms, and degrees Celsius, respectively. One standard measurement has not changed from its traditional roots. That measurement is "time." There are 60 minutes in an hour, 24 hours in a day, 7 days in a week, 52 weeks in a year, 12 months in a year, 365 or 366 days in a year, and so on.

With these different clock or calendar measurement sizes, calculating in time can be difficult and confusing. Many of the units such as the length of a day or the number of days in a year are related to nature. A day is defined as one revolution of Earth. A month originally was determined by one cycle of the moon, and a year is one rotation of Earth around the sun. This may make sense on Earth, but in space these measurements don't really apply.

- Do you think our time system is satisfactory?
- How might you change it?
- What would make sense if you were designing a system for space?

You work for NASA, and your group has been commissioned to design and implement a new system of "time" for space travel. Your new system can be based upon a number of factors. It can be metric or converted to a different clock system, such as 5, 7, or some other number. The system can be a combination of clock systems that might function well together. You should create a system that is reasonable, easy to calculate, adaptable, and practical.

Produce an original report with the following features:

- A complete explanation of your new time system, stating the name of each unit, its relationship to other units, and a means of conversion between standard time units and your new units

- A description and explanation of why you chose your system; why it is easier, reasonable, and useful; and how you might sell your new system to your superiors

- A design for a new clock and/or calendar that will use your system

- A conversion of the following dates and times to your new system:
  October 12, 1492
  July 4, 1776
  December 7, 1941
  November 22, 1963
  January 20, 1993 12:00 P.M.
  the date and time you were born

Selection and Reflection

Webster's Dictionary defines CYCLE as:

cy•cle 1 : an interval of time during which a sequence of a recurring succession of events or phenomena is completed 2 : a course or series of events or operations that recur regularly and usually lead back to the starting point 3: a circular or spiral arrangement 4 : a long period of time : age

Think about the title of this unit, *Cycles*, the definition, and the mathematics you learned in this unit.

- What have you learned about cycles in this unit?

- What do cycles have to do with mathematics?

- What mathematics did you use and learn while doing this unit? Use examples from several of the unit's activities in your explanation.

A Baffling Birthday

The Problem

Teresa is having a party at her house. The group is discussing birthdays and talking about planning parties. After listening for a while, Teresa says, "There is something interesting about my birthday. Two days ago I was 13, but next year I will turn 16." If Teresa is telling the truth, what kind of party is she having? When is her birthday?

The Problem

The *Winner's Circle*, a new TV game show, is coming out next fall. Contestants are selected randomly from the audience. The number of contestants is based on the number of spots in the circle on the stage, which varies with each show. At the announcer's signal, contestants race to the stage and stand on a spot in the circle. Starting with the red spot, the announcer says to the contestant on that spot "you stay." He continues to the next contestant on the right and says "you leave." To the third contestant, he says "you stay," and so on, around and around the circle, asking every other contestant to leave until just one contestant is left. This remaining contestant is the winner.

Suppose you are a contestant on *The Winner's Circle*. If there are 29 spots on the circle, where would you stand in relationship to the red spot to be the winner?

Extension Find a way to determine where to stand in a circle with any number of spots.

"*I Am Thinking of a Number*"

The Problem

What is the least positive number that you can divide by 7 and get a remainder of 4, divide by 8 and get a remainder of 5, and divide by 9 and get a remainder of 6?

The Problem

Shalonda is trying to outwit her brother Ben with a math question. He is allowed only 30 minutes to answer. Before asking the question, Shalonda and Ben agree that if he guesses correctly, then *she* will wash the dinner dishes, and if he guesses incorrectly, then *he* will wash the dishes. Shalonda asks the question: "If you use 8 as a factor 1,007 times, what would be the ones digit in the answer?" What number would Ben have to guess in order to get out of doing the dishes?

Sibling Rivalry

The Problem

Mrs. Bluemel's grandfather clock is broken. The only time it will chime is when the minute hand and the hour hand are at right angles to each other. Each time it does chime, it chimes three times. In a 24-hour day, how many times does it chime?

Tick, Tock, A Broken Clock

The Problem

Walking in Circles

In the land of Spiro, everyone walks in order-3 spirolateral patterns. Within a family, each person has the same numbers in their spirolateral pattern, but the numbers may be in a different order. One day, Mrs. 2-4-5 plans to send one of her children to the grocery store and another one to the post office. If she has a child in every possible number combination of 2, 4, and 5, which child should she send to which store to make sure they get there and back?

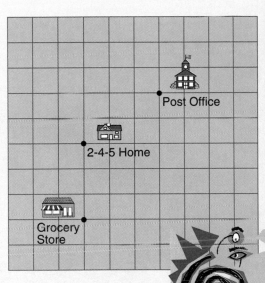

Post Office

2-4-5 Home

Grocery Store

Extension If the people of Spiro walked in order-4 spirolateral patterns, can you think of a problem they would encounter?

A Letter from Mars

The Problem

It is the 22nd century. A human settlement, called Mars City, has been established on the planet Mars. The people of Mars City use the metric, or base-ten, measure of time. The people on Earth, however, still use the standard measure of time.

The mayor of Mars City wants to write a letter to his sister in Los Angeles, California. If the date on Mars is 798 years, 9 weeks, and 9 days, what date should he put on the letter so his sister will know when he wrote it?

TREASURE ISLAND

Looking Ahead

In this unit, you will see how mathematics can be used to answer questions about measurement and angles. You will experience:

▶ giving directions and measuring without standard tools or units

▶ using proportions to determine distances

▶ using a protractor and compass to measure, construct, and bisect angles

▶ determining locations using latitude and longitude

▶ using computer programs to draw geometric figures

Did You Ever Wonder?
What do mathematics and sailing along the northern Atlantic coast have to do with each other? Turn the page and see how Laurie L. Moran of Bangor, Maine, combined the two!

Teens in the News

Featuring: Laurie L. Moran
Age: 17
Hometown: Bangor, Maine
Career Goal: Marine Biology Teacher
Interests: Yearbook editor, tennis

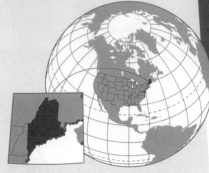

Laurie Moran has always loved the ocean. When she was in the 4th grade, she went on her first whale watch. That experience convinced her to begin her study of marine biology.

In the summer of 1992, Laurie took part in a program to learn about navigation. For five weeks, Laurie and 14 other girls lived and studied on their ship, the Harvey Gamage.

Laurie had experiences she will never forget. She went tide-pooling on Star Island. She used sticks to ward off sea gulls on the Isles of Shoals near the New Hampshire border. Laurie saw humpback whales and even got a picture of a "breach" — a whale jumping totally out of the water!

Laurie took classes in maritime history, nautical science, and marine biology. The girls were responsible for around-the-clock watch duty, which Laurie says was scary at night. The only time anyone was excused from watch duty was when she had galley (kitchen) duty.

During her five-week sail, Laurie learned to use radio signals to determine the ship's longitude and latitude. She used a compass and landmarks to pinpoint their exact location at sea. Laurie also calculated where the ship should sail to reach their next location.

Based on this fantastic experience, Laurie knows she wants to earn a Ph.D. in Science and earn her Captain's License. Laurie's love of the ocean will sail her into an exciting career!

Going Around in Circles Can Keep You on an Even Keel!

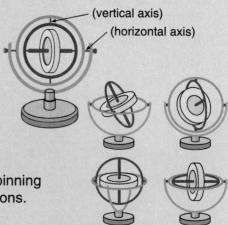

(vertical axis)
(horizontal axis)

Once the gyroscope wheel is spinning the axle resists changing directions.

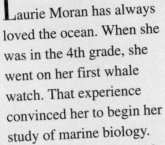

Team Project

Nautical Jargon

Part of what Laurie learned during her five-week sail was the language or "jargon" of sailing. She learned that the kitchen on a ship is called the galley. She also learned that a nautical mile is 6,080 feet, not 5,280 feet.

Research to find as many words as you can that are used in navigation. These words might describe directions, locations, parts of a ship, and types of sails.

Pretend your classroom is your ship. Use nautical jargon to describe the location of each member of your team.

1519
Magellan leaves Spain to sail around the world.

1768
Jeanne Bare, disguised as a boy, becomes the first woman to sail around the world.

1794
Prime Meridian fixed at Greenwich Observatory, England.

1908
Gyrocompass developed to aid navigation.

1500 **1600** **1800** **2000**

1757
Captain John Campbell creates the sextant.

1813
First liquid-filled compass

1992
Laurie Moran takes part in Tall Ships Parade, New York Harbor.

For more information

If you would like more information about learning to navigate a ship, contact:

American Sail Training Association
P. O. Box 1459
Newport, Rhode Island
02840

You can learn more about the math Laurie uses in sailing by completing the activities in this unit.

Setting the Scene

MATHEMATICS TOOLKIT

Many professions require the use of tools. This mathematics toolkit includes tools that you may find useful as you study this unit. At times you may feel lost or not know where to begin when presented with a problem situation. Take time to read this toolkit to see the different measurement tools and problem-solving strategies the characters in the script used. You don't need to wait until your teacher tells you how to set up a proportion when using map scales or how to measure angles. Instead, if it seems like it might work, try it.

Narrator: Five students in the drama club are rehearsing a skit they wrote after reading *Treasure Island,* by Robert Louis Stevenson.

(in a hushed voice): Four old salts gather on a London dock. Crates and barrels are stacked high ready to be loaded. From a distance, one might think they were discussing the lore of seafarers: the great storm, the great calm, tales of triumph or calamity. But that was not the nature of their discussion. These four had sailed together and shared many secrets.

Jake: I don't know who's the greater fool, the one who called us here, or us for showing up!

Mary: Aye, it better be good. It's dangerous for us to be seen together. If the authorities put two and two together, our next meeting will be at the execution dock.

Mary: Aye, all those years of pirating and what have we got?

Roberta: Belay that talk!

Narrator: A fifth figure emerges from his hiding place among the crates. He speaks.

Jim: Glad you'll be 'tis Gentleman Jim hearing such talk! If it'd been an agent, you'd swing for sure.

Will: Thar's none but us left alive. So, who's to know?

Roberta: Some escaped with treasure.

Jake: For risking our necks, this better be worthwhile!

Will: That's more than we can say!

Jim: What's old Gentleman Jim diggin' up his old mates fer, says you? Thankin' me, you'll be, for it's the rest of the captain's treasure I'm after.

Will: What's left of the captain's treasure is already back in England.

Jake: Aye, dug up and probably spent by now.

Will: We've all seen the captain's map. Written on it in the mate's own hand was "Bulk of treasure here."

Jim: Aye, in the mate's own hand. It was the bulk of the treasure, but not all of it. The jewels weren't on the map. I was with him at the end and I took this map from his sea chest.

(He pulls out a rolled up map.)

It says, "Walk two dozen paces east of the tree nearest the entrance of the cave, and there you will find the jewels." And how far do you suppose that is, mates?

Roberta: The captain was taller than I, sir. Perhaps, if I took two dozen *giant* steps, the length would be about the same as the captain's paces.

Narrator: Walking is one way to estimate distance. Adults may use a long stride to estimate a distance of one yard. What other ways do you know that someone may estimate the length of an inch, a foot, or a yard?

Jim: Aye, look at this, mate. At the bottom of the map, it says that the distance between the trees located on either side of the cave is the same as ten of the captain's paces.

Mary: That's just like a key to a map. Sometimes they say things like "1 inch represents 50 miles."

Stop the Script!
Discuss ways to estimate length. Also, estimate the distance covered by two dozen paces.

Stop the Script!
Discuss how the sailors could use the information to figure out the distance to the buried treasure.

Roberta: Let's see, I can walk the distance between the two trees in 12 steps. It only took the captain 10. I can set up a proportion comparing my steps to the captain's.

$$\text{paces between trees} \atop \text{paces to treasure} \quad \frac{12}{x} = \frac{10}{12} \quad {\text{paces between trees} \atop \text{paces to treasure}}$$

I remember that the product of the means (x times 10) is equal to the product of the extremes (12 times 12). Using mathematical shorthand, $10x = 12(12)$ or $10x = 144$.

I can find the number of paces by dividing both sides of the equation by 10. That shows that $x = 14.4$ or $14\frac{2}{5}$ steps. I should take *about* 14-and-a-half steps to locate the buried treasure.

Jim: Well, blow me down, mate. That's pretty good figurin'. You think you're so smart — how do we know which direction to walk?

Roberta: If we dug in a circular pattern $14\frac{1}{2}$ paces from the center, we could check to see if there is buried treasure.

Jake: Why would we want to dig in a circle? You've been at sea too long!

Mary: The map says to walk east. I remember how to determine direction. The sun rises in the east. In the morning, we can get up before dawn and walk in the direction the sun rises. That will keep us from having to dig so much for the buried treasure.

Jim: At night, we could locate the north star. We could draw a line in the dirt and call that 0°. In the morning, we could turn east toward the sunrise. That means we have turned to the right 90°. A 90° angle looks like the corner of a square.

Have you ever heard of a protractor? It can be used to measure angles.

Will: Aye, the old salts used to tell tales of turning different degrees to find the directions to new locations.

They talked about acute angles. They were little turns, you know, between 0° and 90°.

Jim: Aye, mate, like this.

Narrator: He drew in the dirt.

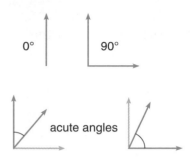

acute angles

Jake: Yeah, I know what a right angle is. Ya hold your right arm straight out beside you and point. Then you turn and go in that direction. That's a right angle.

Will: And I suppose if you hold your left arm out, it's a left angle?

Narrator: An angle of 180° can be imagined by holding both arms out from your sides. It is called a straight angle.

Stop the Script!
Discuss how to measure angles using your protractor.

Jim: I have a question about these protractors. How can you tell which set of numbers to use?

Mary: One side of the angle is at 0°. From there, read the numbers just like you were counting—10, 20, 30, and so on—until you reach the other side of the angle.

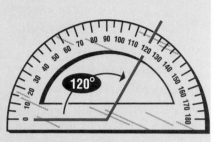

120°

Jim: Thar's just one more thing—how do we find the island again? I warn't the navigator of the ship that took us there.

Roberta: I heard some say that the port on the island was at 77° 15' West, 18° North. Them are the latitude and longitude of the island.

Will: I think I remember. Lines of latitude, or parallels, are imaginary lines circling Earth parallel to each other and the equator. Lines of longitude, or meridians, are imaginary lines running from the north pole to the south pole. They cross the parallels of latitude at right angles. Together they are used on maps to help sailors locate places.

Longitude 77° 15' West is between 77° and 78° west of the prime meridian in Greenwich, England. There are 60 minutes in a degree, so it is about $\frac{15}{60}$ or one-fourth of the way from 77° to 78°. Latitude 18° North is north of the equator. We can look in an atlas.

Jim: I'm sure we can find the treasure now. But, perhaps, you'd like to sleep first, and tomorrow...

This concludes the Mathematics Toolkit. It included many mathematical tools for you to use throughout this unit. As you work through this unit, you should use these tools to help you solve problems. You may want to explain how to use these mathematical tools in your journal. Or you may want to create a toolkit notebook to add mathematical tools you discover throughout this unit.

Sailing by the Sun

The Polynesian navigators of the Pacific Basin sailed without maps across huge stretches of open ocean. They were very aware of their ocean environment. Changes in the current, the color of the water, and the way clouds behave over land, all provided information regarding their location. In addition, they observed the sun, the winds, and the flights of shorebirds. They also used various kinds of compasses to guide them.

How aware of your surroundings are you? What kind of information is available to you as you travel in your neighborhood?

Work with a partner on the following activity.

Without using the typical units of measure, such as feet, yards, or miles, describe for a new student in your school how to go from school to another location, such as a video store. You may use street names if you wish, but you must include other information as well. Use mathematical tools and reasoning to present a route that is reasonable.

Write a brief report describing the route, the mathematical tools you used, and why you chose that route. Be prepared to present your report to the class.

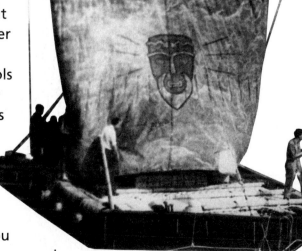

Blazing the Trail
Getting Your Bearings

*F*old a piece of paper to make four **right angles** in the center of the page. The point where the angles meet is the **vertex** of each angle. Label the fold at the top center of the page 0°.

- If you make a turn from the 0° line to the right until it reaches the next fold line, a rotation, or turn, of how many degrees has been made?
- What angle measures are shown by the other folds? Label the measures of the angles.
- Make additional folds to find the measures of at least ten different angles. Label the measures of the angles.
- How did you determine the angle measure to each fold line you made?
- A tool that measures angles is called a **protractor.** Your folded paper can be a protractor. Describe how you developed your protractor and how you could use it to measure angles.
- Write down at least six angle measures. Use the protractor you developed to draw angles with those measures. Explain how you used your homemade protractor to measure the angles.
- Find three objects in your classroom or school that include angles other than 90°, 180°, 270°, or 360°. Identify the objects. Draw a diagram showing the angles represented in each of the objects. Explain how you know, before measuring, that the angles do not measure 90°, 180°, 270°, or 360°. Then describe how you measured the angles.

Bridging the Gap

Your community wants to build a bridge across a river. Your group is responsible for determining the length, or **span,** of the bridge. There are no rulers, tape measures, or other measuring devices available. Suppose that the span of the bridge is the same as the distance from one side of your classroom to the opposite wall. (You may also choose two other points to represent the span of the bridge.)

Parts of the body, like the width of a finger or the length of a forearm, are sometimes used as units of length. People may also count **paces,** or strides, to measure length. When using paces as a unit of measure, try to walk in a normal manner so that your steps are relatively uniform in length.

- Using your own pace as your unit of length, explain how to find the distance from one side of your classroom to the other.
- In your group, discuss the number of paces needed. Were they the same or different for each person? What factors might affect the length of an individual's stride or pace?
- Suppose you are leaving instructions for a friend who is very short, and you are very tall. What information could you give your friend to help him or her build a bridge the same length as that which you measured? Explain the changes they might need to make to adapt the length of their stride to the length you used in the instructions.
- Repeat the activity above using the length of your hand as the unit of measure.

Mall Measures

In your group, choose two of the situations below to complete.

Situation 1

You and your friends are planning to go shopping. Write instructions for your friends for getting from your school or home to the place you plan to shop.

Explain to your friends where to start and how to get to the shopping area. Assume that your friends have no measuring instruments available. Describe how to measure the distances and direction of travel. Include more than just street names.

Situation 2

Describe several different ways to measure without using a ruler or other traditional measuring devices. Include methods that are appropriate for measuring long distances, as well as short distances.

Situation 3

Select an object in your school or home that has a measure greater than your height. Choose a nonstandard method for measuring the object. Explain how you measured the object and how you could use this method to measure another object about the same size.

Situation 4

Choose an object, like the width of your hand or the length of your shoe, to represent one unit of measure. Measure at least three different objects using your "ruler". Sketch and label the measurements. Describe the differences you might find if you compared your measurements with another student using his or her "ruler".

The Footpath

Your friend has arrived on Treasure Island and will be walking to your camp using a map that you nailed to a tree by the landing. How can you give directions so that your friend can easily find you? The only materials available are the map, a ruler, a pen or pencil, and some paper.

- Decide on a scale for the map.

- Explain how your friend can measure the actual land distances.

- Tell your friend what direction to travel and how far to go before changing direction. (Your route must avoid the hazards marked on the map.)

- Use angle measures to describe turns. Explain how your friend can measure the angle of a turn.

- What factors influenced your decisions in recommending the route?

Far and Away

On Treasure Island, Anna Maria walked fifty paces from camp to reach the ocean. Her brother walked only thirty-two paces to cover the same distance.

Is the length of your pace different from someone else's? How can you compare the lengths?

- Make a map using at least five locations at your school. Let one member of your group pace the distances between the locations. Outline the distances on the map based on that person's pace. The key at the bottom of the map might read "10 paces = distance from the door of the room to the file cabinet."

- Using only the information on the map, draw a new map that shows distances based on a different group member's pace. The paces of the two group members should be different. Explain how your group determined the distances for the revised map.

- Measure a distance of 25 feet. Compare that distance to the key on one of your maps. Estimate the distances in feet represented on the map. Explain how you estimated those distances.

- Prepare a 3- to 5-minute group presentation on your map of the school. Explain the locations that are marked on your map, the key to the original map, how the distances changed when a different pace was used, and how the distances in feet were estimated using the 25-foot measure as a reference point.

Fantasy Island

Imagine that your ship sank and you are marooned on an island.

- Draw a map of your island on a piece of poster board.
- Identify the directions north, south, east, and west on the map.
- Use a coin to draw circles representing at least six landmarks on your island. Label the landmarks.
- Draw a length at the bottom of the map to represent one unit of measure. Label the scale of the map.

Your map will be a game board. Mark a starting place somewhere on the map. The object of the game will be to move around the game board until all landmarks have been visited.

Play the game on your game board. Use the rules for the game that your teacher will give you.

When you have finished the game, complete the following.

- Describe your strategy for estimating the distance and angle of movement.
- Explain your reason for choosing a large or small distance to represent one unit. Describe how using a much larger or much smaller unit of measure would change the strategy you used to play the game.

80° 3' West, 19° 41' North

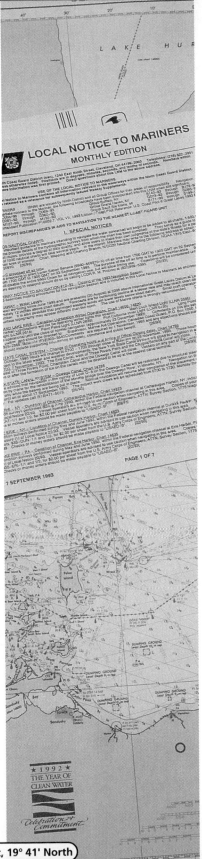

> "...and there fell out the map of an island, with latitude and longitude, soundings, names of hills, and bays, and inlets, and every particular that would be needed to bring a ship to a safe anchorage upon its shores." *Treasure Island,* Robert Louis Stevenson

The captain hid the jewels on an island. The only clue he left to the island's identity was: longitude 80° 3' West, latitude 19° 41' North.

Use the information 80° 3' West, 19° 41' North to find the location of the island. Use the information in Longitude and Latitude and The Island in your Data Bank along with maps or atlases to determine the name of the island.

Prepare a summary of your findings.

- Explain how your group discovered the name of the island and how you verified that this was the right location.
- Describe the location, referencing other nearby islands.

Be prepared to make an oral presentation to the class.

THE PATHFINDERS

The captain of your ship has given you some instructions for paths that must be followed very carefully. Your task is to make a drawing of these paths. If you aren't careful, you will have to swab the deck!

Use a protractor to measure angles. One person will pace according to the instructions. Place the protractor to determine the direction of movement. The direction the pacer is facing before each turn is considered 0°. Stretch a string to indicate the direction of movement. Pace the indicated number of steps. Sketch the results of each path on graph paper before beginning the next set of instructions.

A
turn right 30°, go 12 paces
turn right 150°, go 7 paces
turn right 30°, go 12 paces
turn right 150°, go 7 paces

B
turn left 60°, go 8 paces
turn left 120°, go 4 paces
turn left 120°, go 8 paces
turn right 120°, go 4 paces

C
turn right 135°, go 11 paces
turn left 90°, go 11 paces
turn left 45°, go 8 paces
turn left 90°, go 8 paces
turn left 45°, go 11 paces

D
turn right 60°, go 9 paces
turn right 120°, go 9 paces
turn right 120°, go 9 paces

E
turn right 90°, go 10 paces
turn right 45°, go 3 paces
turn right 90°, go 3 paces
turn right 45°, go 10 paces
turn right 45°, go 3 paces
turn right 90°, go 3 paces

F
turn left 18°, go 5 paces
turn right 72°, go 5 paces
turn right 72°, go 5 paces
turn right 72°, go 5 paces
turn right 72°, go 5 paces

Now it's your turn to write the instructions. Write three sets. One set of instructions should make a path that forms a rectangle. Another set should form a triangle. The third set should form a different polygon of your choosing.

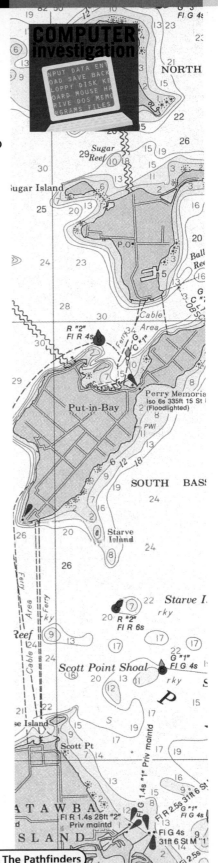

Type the following commands. Find the degree measure of turn and distance for the path that closes the figure (returns to the starting point). Sketch each figure on a piece of paper and label the angles of turn.

- DRAW
  RT 60 FD 80
  RT 120 FD 80

- DRAW
  PU FD 90 PD RT 135 FD 90
  RT 90 FD 90

The angles of turn in the above figures are the **exterior angles** of the figure. Look at the sum of the exterior angles of the figures you have drawn. Describe any patterns that you find.

Use LOGO to draw a path that forms a rectangle. Explain how you know from the instructions that the figure is a rectangle. How would you change the instructions to form a square?

Describe any patterns you find in the measures of the exterior angles.

Use LOGO to draw these figures.

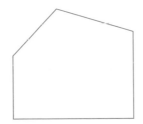

Describe any patterns you find in the measures of the exterior angles.

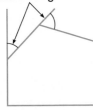

Exterior angles

Draw at least two figures of your own. Make rough sketches of the path around each figure. Write instructions in LOGO for drawing the paths. Explain the strategies you used to determine the direction of movement.

COMPUTER investigation

Type the LOGO commands shown at the right. Sketch the resulting figure.

```
DRAW
RT 30 FD 60
RT 60 FD 16
RT 120 FD 60
RT 60 FD 16
```

- Double the length of each side in the figure. Use LOGO to draw the new figure. Sketch the figure.
- Add 10 units to the length of each side in the original figure. Use LOGO to draw the new figure. Sketch the figure.
- Compare the figures you have drawn to the original figure. Which figure looks most like the original figure? Explain.

Use LOGO to draw a closed figure of your choice. Sketch the figure. For each alteration below, sketch the resulting figure, describe the changes you made, and describe the effects of that alteration.

Alteration 1

Increase the size of your figure by multiplying the length of each side by the same number. Which numbers could you choose that would fit this description? Sketch the resulting figure.

Alteration 2

Decrease the size of your original figure by multiplying the length of each side by the same number. Which numbers could you choose that would fit this description? Sketch the resulting figure.

Alteration 3

Increase the size of your original figure by adding the same amount to the length of each side.

Write a report stating the properties of closed figures that you have discovered during your investigation of paths and the effects of alterations on them. Include comments about the exterior angles of the figures.

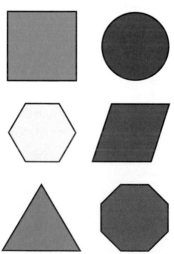

Adventures at Sea
Buried Treasure

MENU
station
A

As you sit on the beach and your eyes wash over the ocean, you notice a bottle bobbing in the water. You wade into the water, recover the bottle, and open it. Inside is a message. It seems to be in code. Could it contain a clue to help you locate the buried treasure?

ZC GWN LHJ NJTXIUQHJT QOZU PXU-
UHKX, GWN LHJ CZJT QOX QIXHUNIX.

KW QW QOX QHMM QIXXU. QOX CZIUQ
QIXX ZU QOX SIWJK WJX. UW ZU QOX
UXLWJT. QOX QOZIT QIXX ZU JXHIMG
QSW ONJTIXT CXXQ QHMM, HJT LHUQU
H SZTX UOHTWS. ZQ LHJ FX XHUZMG
UXXJ CIWP QOX UXH, FWQO WJ QOX
XHUQ HJT QOX SXUQ, HJT PZKOO FX
NUXT HU H MHJTPHIV WJ H PHE. QOX
KWMT ZU FNIZXT FXJXHQO ZQU
UEIXHTZJK UOHTWS.

Use the information on letter frequency in your Data Bank to help decipher the coded message.

- Describe the strategy you used to decipher the coded message.
- Explain how decoding the message uses the mathematical concept of proportions.

MENU station B

The Great Fish Story

Some people who were fishing just arrived from the sea. They describe a fish that got away as the biggest they had ever seen. "Why, it was at least twelve times as long as that fish in the picture!" said a weather-tarnished seaman, as he pointed toward the wall.

Imagine that all dimensions of the fish increased by a factor of twelve. Use the fish picture your teacher gives you as a model for the fish.

- Explain how large the fish would be according to the seaman's description.
- Would the fish fit in your classroom?
- How many people might it take to hoist the fish from the water?
- Estimate how much larger the cross-section of the actual fish would be than the area of the cross-section of the fish in the picture.
- How do you think the fish's weight would compare if the fish in the picture weighs 15 pounds? Defend your answer with words and diagrams.

The Fork in the Footpath

Lisa has found a treasure map that says, "At the fork in the footpath, turn half the angle of the fork." She knows that the location of the treasure is very precise. Help her find a way to halve the angle.

On a large piece of paper, use string to make an angle to represent the fork in the path. Tape the vertex and the end of each side of the string angle to hold them in place.

Use a string compass (a length of string tied to a pencil) to draw an arc that intersects both sides of the angle. What is true about the distance from the vertex of the angle to each point where the arc intersects the side of the angle?

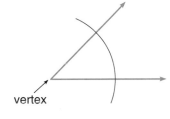

vertex

From each of those points, draw an arc inside the angle, each using the same amount of string on the compass. The two arcs that you have drawn should intersect.

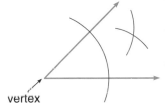

vertex

Tape a piece of string between the vertex and the point where the arcs intersect.

- Measure the two angles that have been formed. What relationship do they have?

- On a piece of paper, draw at least three angles of varying measures. Use a standard compass to duplicate the process on paper that you used with the string. Measure the pairs of angles that are formed. Is there a pattern to the results?

- Explain in your own words how to bisect an angle and why you think the procedure works.

Let's Face It

Lydia has found a treasure map that says, "Face the big tree, then turn to face the rock. Now turn again the same amount and you will see the location of the treasure." Help Lydia find a way to exactly copy the angle of the turn.

On a large piece of paper, use string to make an angle to represent the turn from the tree to the rock. Tape the vertex and the end of each side of the angle to hold them in place. Tape another piece of string beside the angle to represent a ray.

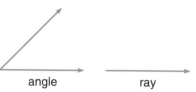

Use a string compass (a length of string tied to a pencil) to draw an arc that cuts both sides of the angle. Using the same length of string, draw an arc from the endpoint of the ray that cuts the ray and extends past the point where you estimate the other side of the angle will be.

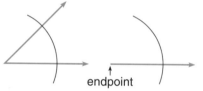

Use a length of string to measure the distance between the points where the arc cuts both sides of the angle. Mark that same distance on the arc for the second angle. Tape a length of string between the endpoint of the ray and the point where the arcs intersect.

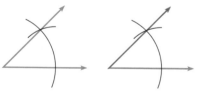

- Measure the two angles. What relationship do they have?
- On a piece of paper, draw at least two angles of different measures. Use a standard compass to duplicate the process on paper that you used with the string, and copy each angle.
- Explain in your own words how to copy an angle and why you think the procedure works.
- Describe how you could double the size of an angle.

Between a Rock and a Hard Place

Lu Chan has found a treasure map that says, "Make a triangle of equal sides with one side being the length between the big tree and the big rock. The treasure is buried at the third point of the triangle." Help Lu Chan find a way to construct an equilateral triangle.

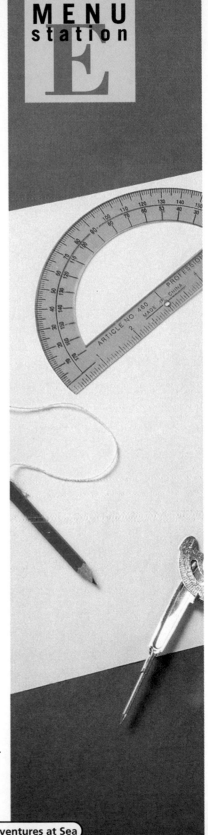

On a large piece of paper, tape a length of string to represent the distance between the tree and the rock. Make a string compass (a length of string tied to a pencil) that is the same length as the string on the paper.

Remember that an equilateral triangle has three equal-length sides. Think of a way to use the string compass to draw an equilateral triangle using the taped string as one side.

- Describe your method of constructing an equilateral triangle. Explain how you know that the triangle is equilateral and why your method works.
- Use pencil, paper, and a standard compass to construct at least three equilateral triangles of different sizes. Use a ruler and a protractor to measure the sides and angles in each triangle. What relationships exist?

What's Your Angle?

Before naval architects begin to design a ship, they consider some of the same things a residential architect does before designing a house. That's because the inner framework of a ship's hull resembles the rafters supporting the roof of a house.

Your group has been hired to build the rafters of a house. The master planner says that only 30° angles are needed. Another contractor says that 45° angles are stronger. What should you do? You know how to construct an equilateral triangle and how to bisect angles.

- Sketch the side view of several different plans for the rafters of a house showing how different angles might be used. Explain why you think the roofs of most houses are not at a 90° angle with the walls of the building. Describe what angles you think would be most useful in building a house and why.

- If your only tools are a straightedge, pencils, and paper clips, describe how you could bisect an angle. Write an explanation of your method and tell why it works.

- Explain how to construct angles of 15°, 30°, 45°, 60°, and 90° using only a straightedge and a compass.

- Devise a plan to test which angles would be stronger in building rafters. Your only available building materials will be a roll of tape and a box of toothpicks or straws.

- Develop a blueprint or plan that shows how the rafters are constructed, the angles that are included, and a rationale for why you selected that design.

- Prepare a 3- to 5-minute presentation to the class that outlines how you tested the strength of the structure and what you learned.

Another contractor wants you to build the rafters for a barn using only isosceles triangles (triangles that have two angles of equal measure). You need to explore angle relationships before drawing the plan for the rafters.

Construct figures that match the following descriptions. Use only a straightedge and a compass for the constructions. Use a ruler to measure the lengths of the sides of the figures.

- Draw three triangles that each contain two 45° angles. Describe any relationships or patterns you observe.
- Write a ratio comparing the length of the longer side to the length of the shorter sides in each triangle. Make a hypothesis about your observation.
- Describe how you could draw a triangle that contains two 45° angles without measuring the angles.
- Can you construct an isosceles triangle that does not contain a right angle? Explain. Use diagrams to support your reasoning. Is the ratio of the longer side to the shorter sides the same as it was when you had a 90° angle? Explain.
- Develop a blueprint or plan that shows how the barn rafters are to be constructed.

Buried Treasure

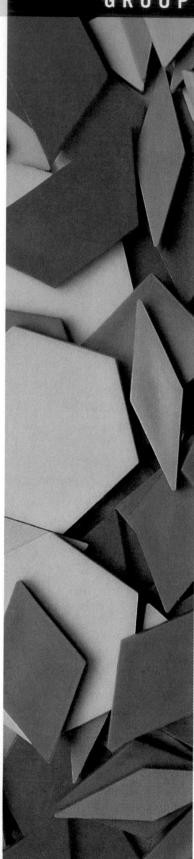

"The doctor opened the seals with great care, and there fell out a map of the island, with latitude and longitude, soundings, names of hills, and bays, and inlets, and every particular that would be needed to bring a ship to a safe anchorage upon its shores. It was about nine miles long and five across, shaped, you might say, like a fat dragon standing up, and had two fine land-locked harbors, and a hill in the center part marked 'The Spy-glass.' There were several additions of a later date; but, above all, three crosses of red ink — two on the north part of the island, one in the southwest, and, besides this last, in the same red ink and in a small, neat hand, very different from the captain's tottery characters, these words: 'Bulk of treasure here.'" *Treasure Island,* Robert Louis Stevenson

Design your own treasure island using pattern blocks. Then trace the island on paper to make a map. Identify forts, villages, or other landmarks. Decide on a location to "bury" the treasure.

Write a set of at least eight clues for finding the treasure. Each clue should take the searcher to a different location on your island, where he or she will find the next clue. Your first clue should tell the searcher where to begin. Indicate the direction and number of units for each move. The searcher's only tools will be the map and the clues—no protractors or rulers allowed!

Exchange island maps and clues with another group. Follow their clues to the treasure.

Describe the relationships among the angles and sides of the pattern block pieces you used to create your island.

YOUR REPORT

Prepare a written group report on your treasure island and your investigation of the pattern blocks.

- ● Include how you measured lengths and angles, and any problems you experienced in following another group's clues.

- ● Describe the shortest route from your starting point to the treasure location, and tell how you determined that route.

- ● Calculate the ratio of the measures of the sides in each of the pattern block pieces.

- ● Measure the interior angles of each pattern block piece. Calculate the ratio of the angle measures between pairs of pattern block pieces.

Tracking the Treasure

Your school has become a treasure island inhabited by several teams of students. Your team's task is to develop a treasure map of your school identifying key landmarks. These landmarks should be ones that require the use of the map to find. The "treasure" will be an object located somewhere in your school, for example, a particular set of books in the library. Your map will be used by another team.

Select a starting location. Identify a unit to be used, such as a pace, a foot, or a hand. Give a method for comparing the unit with a known amount, such as "ten paces are the same as the width of this room." The location of the "treasure" on the map should be clearly recognizable when it is reached. For example, a note could be given to the treasure hunters by a specific teacher at that location, or, the last clue could give a hint about the final location. Be creative in determining a way for the treasure hunters to know when they have located the treasure without asking the team that developed the map.

After your team has developed its map and tracked the treasure from another team's map, prepare a report with the following features.

- An explanation of the methods you think would be most effective in developing a map to an unknown location
- A copy of the treasure map you developed marked with any changes that you would make after completing this investigation
- A description and explanation of how the nonstandard units of measure that you used could be translated into standard units of measure
- The actual measures represented on your map using standard units as well as nonstandard units
- A description of the role that both standard and nonstandard units have in our world
- Information on how directional instructions can be verified using angle measure related to a polygon

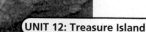

Selection and Reflection

- What was your favorite activity in this unit? Describe why you liked the activity and what you learned from it.
- What mathematics did you use in this unit?
- How can you use what you learned from this unit in your life?

Bridging The Gap

The Problem

The sales associates at DynaTech went to a local camp for teamwork training. At the camp, they were given challenges that they had to work together to complete. Their final task was to construct a bridge across a river 5 meters wide. An unlimited supply of identical boards 4 meters long were provided, but no nails could be used. The bridge had to be made only by piling the boards one on another. The team quickly discovered that if more than half of the weight of the bridge is over the water, the bridge will fall in. Construct a bridge that the team could use. What is the least number of boards the team members could use to span the river?

The Problem

Andy and Zoe chose to do their science fair project on astronomy. As part of their project, they would like to make a scale model of Earth, the moon, and the sun. They will use a styrofoam ball with a diameter of 2 centimeters to represent Earth.

Find the sizes of the styrofoam balls that Andy and Zoe will need for the moon and the sun and the distances they should allow between each of the parts of the model. What kind of problems will Andy and Zoe run into?

The Sky's the Limit

	Diameter	Average Distance from Earth
Earth	8,000 miles	0 miles
Moon	2,200 miles	240,000 miles
Sun	864,000 miles	93,000,000 miles

Spooky Spelunking

The Problem

Tina and Maria are avid spelunkers (cave explorers). Most of the caves they explore have many chambers with one, two, or more openings in and out of them. The cave they just entered is very strange. After they go through any opening, a boulder or pile of rocks falls into the opening, closing the pathway behind them. Tina and Maria are excellent spelunkers and can eventually find their way out of any room or chamber if all of the openings are not blocked. Determine whether it will be possible for them to escape the strange cave shown or whether they will become trapped in one of the chambers.

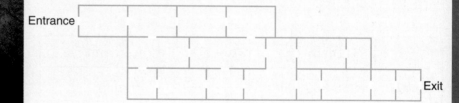

Entrance

Exit

Extension Draw a new cave from which a person could always escape and a cave in which a person might become trapped.

The Problem

A pirate found a treasure chest containing silver coins. He gave $\frac{1}{3}$ of the coins to his first mate. The first mate gave half of her coins to the galley cook. The galley cook gave $\frac{1}{6}$ of his coins to the crew members. If each of the 20 crew members received 3 coins, how many coins were in the treasure chest?

Treasure Found

Turnabout is Fair Play

The Problem

Emily told her friends that she could rotate a book 180° and then rotate it 180° again and have the book end up 90° to its original position.

Emily's friends tried it but couldn't find a way. How can Emily do it?

The Problem

Find a path to the center of the maze in the equilateral triangle below.

Enter Here

The Problem

Numbers of dots that can be arranged as different geometric figures are called figurate numbers. The study of figurate numbers began with the Pythagoreans, a group of Greek mathematicians from 540 B.C. The triangular, square, and pentagonal numbers are the first three sets of figurate numbers. The first four members of these sets are shown below. Draw the first four hexagonal numbers.

Triangular numbers

1   3   6   10

Square numbers

1   4   9   16

Pentagonal numbers

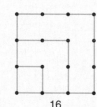

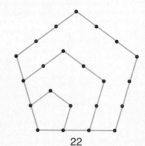

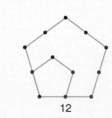

1   5   12   22

TABLE OF CONTENTS

The braille cell, an arrangement of six dots, is the basic unit for reading and writing braille. Sixty-three different patterns are possible from these six dots.

For purposes of identification and description, these dots are numbered downward 1-2-3 on the left and 4-5-6 on the right.

1 . . 4
2 . . 5
3 . . 6

The first ten letters of the alphabet (a-j) use only the dots in the upper two rows of the cell.

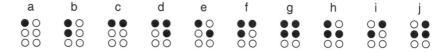

a   b   c   d   e   f   g   h   i   j

The next ten letters of the alphabet (k-t) are formed by adding dot 3 to each of the first ten letters.

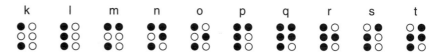

k   l   m   n   o   p   q   r   s   t

The remaining letters (except for w) are formed by adding dots 3 and 6 to each of the first five letters.

u   v   x   y   z   w

The letter *w* is an exception because the French alphabet did not contain a *w* when the code was created; the symbol for *w* was added later.

The numeral sign preceding the first ten letters of the alphabet makes the signs for numerals 1-9 and 0.

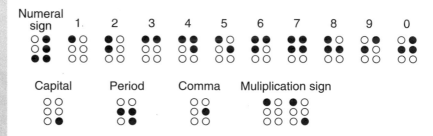

Numeral sign 1 2 3 4 5 6 7 8 9 0

Capital   Period   Comma   Muliplication sign

Year	Pounds
1973	383,000,000
1974	401,000,000
1975	393,000,000
1976	415,000,000
1977	450,000,000
1978	486,000,000
1979	520,000,000
1980	568,000,000
1981	600,000,000
1982	611,000,000
1983	618,000,000
1984	630,000,000
1985	670,000,000
1986	700,000,000
1987	741,000,000
1988	807,000,000
1989	872,000,000
1990	938,000,000
1991	1,031,800,000
1992	1,124,600,000

Americans consume 18 billion quarts of popped popcorn annually or 71 quarts per man, woman and child. Approximately 70 percent is eaten in the home (home popped and pre-popped) and about 30 percent outside the home (theaters, stadiums, schools, and so on). Unpopped popcorn accounts for approximately 90 percent of sales for home consumption.

Major popcorn producing states are Illinois, Indiana, Iowa, Kansas, Kentucky, Michigan, Missouri, Nebraska, and Ohio. The peak period for popcorn sales for home consumption is the fall. Sales remain fairly high throughout the winter months then taper off during the spring and summer. The area of top popcorn consumption is the Midwest region.

Almost all the popcorn consumed throughout the world is grown in the United States. Americans consume more popcorn than the citizens of any other country.

Source: *The Popcorn Institute*, 1993

A Story of the Tangram

There are several stories or legends about the origin of tangrams. One of these stories is about a man named Tan.

Tan lived in China about 4000 years ago, and he owned a beautiful ceramic tile. He valued his tile and decided to show this special tile to the emperor. Unfortunately, Tan tripped as he was going to see the emperor and dropped the tile. The tile broke into 7 pieces. Of course, Tan was devastated. He spent the rest of his life trying to put his tile back into its original shape of a square.

According to the story, Tan was never able to put the tile back into its original shape, but he did make many interesting pictures and designs. Tan shared his broken tile and its many shapes with his friends who visited him. Everyone liked making pictures with the pieces. Tan particularly liked the picture of his cat that he made, as well as the pagoda that resembled the one where he often went to meditate.

The puzzle of the tiles did not die with Tan. Instead it grew in popularity as it was passed on from one generation to the next and from one country to another. Legend says that Napoleon used tangrams to help calm himself while he was imprisoned on St. Helena.

A famous puzzle expert by the name of Sam Loyd wrote about tangrams in the early 1900's. Tangrams can be as simple as shapes cut out of paper or as elaborate as a fancy wood-carved set. Whatever you use, tangrams will open a world of creativity. Perhaps you will understand why tangrams can be a special gift to someone with an imagination.

(in thousands of 42-lb units)					
Varieties	**1988**	**1989**	**1990**	**1991**	**1992**
Red Delicious	88,300	104,080	101,250	98,160	108,690
Golden Delicious	36,360	37,170	36,550	33,775	39,060
Granny Smith	12,010	15,250	15,550	15,650	16,830
Rome	13,790	13,260	13,200	13,610	15,230
McIntosh	15,330	14,780	14,650	15,040	16,810
Jonathan	8,320	8,590	8,170	8,770	9,160
York	7,000	5,620	5,550	6,900	6,720
Idared	3,350	3,880	3,550	4,130	5,060
Fuji	N/A	N/A	N/A	N/A	N/A
Gala	N/A	N/A	N/A	N/A	N/A
Newtown	3,930	4,350	4,300	3,800	4,470
Stayman	4,710	4,210	4,100	4,800	4,200
Empire	N/A	1,750	2,350	3,060	3,240
R.I. Greening	2,250	3,020	2,320	2,740	3,690
Winesap	3,520	3,630	3,310	3,770	3,480
Cortland	2,550	2,190	2,220	2,300	2,710
Gravenstein	1,850	2,140	2,200	2,000	2,180
Northern Spy	2,400	2,630	2,000	2,630	2,340
All Others	11,664	10,680	9,596	10,510	11,357
Total	217,334	237,210	230,876	231,635	255,227

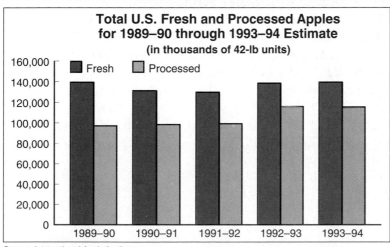

Total U.S. Fresh and Processed Apples for 1989–90 through 1993–94 Estimate
(in thousands of 42-lb units)

Source: International Apple Institute

Brand and Model: Newest models of mountain bikes.

Price: Manufacturer's suggested retail price

Weight: All tested bikes had a 19- or 20-inch frame.

Shifting ease: How easy it was to change gears while riding. Rated on a five-point scale (1–5) with 5 being the easiest.

Brakes Dry and Wet: How quickly each bicycle went from 15 mph to 0 mph, using both brakes. Rated on a five-point scale (1–5) with 5 being the quickest.

Brake Control: How smoothly the brakes responded. Rated on a five-point scale (1–5) with 5 being the best.

Handling (On-Road and Off-Road): Each bike was tested through a series of maneuvers in both on-road and off-road conditions. Rated on a five-point scale (1–5) with 5 being the best.

Shock Absorption: Each bike was tested by riding it along a 48-foot "ladder" at about 7 mph and judged how severely the bumps were felt through the seat and handlebars. Rated on a five-point scale (1–5) with 5 being the best.

Coasting: Each bike was timed coasting down a steep downhill section of road for one-half mile. Rated on a five-point scale (1–5) with 5 being the best.

Seat Comfort: Men and women testers made this judgment after riding the bikes along a 48-foot ladder. Rated on a five-point scale (1–5) with 5 being the best.

Gear Range: A large range means a more versatile bike. The numbers in this column indicate the number of inches the bike will move with one complete turn of the pedals (in the lowest and highest gear).

Frame Sizes: The smallest and largest frames available. Manufacturers usually make frames in 2-inch increments.

Brand and Model	Price $	Weight lb.	Shifting Ease	Brakes Dry	Brakes Wet	Brake Control
Bianchi Boardwalk	414	29	4	5	3	4
Cannondale SH400	479	28.5	5	4	4	5
Diamond Black	264	33.25	3	5	5	4
Giant Innova	370	27.5	4	4	4	3
Miyata Triple Cross	425	28.75	4	4	3	3
Nishiki Saga 510	510	27.75	5	4	3	5
Peugeot Limestone	350	31.5	4	5	4	4
Raleigh Eclipse CX	262	31	3	4	3	4
Ross Mt. Olympus XC	260	30	3	4	3	2
Schwinn Crisscross	310	29	5	4	2	5
Specialized Crossroads	350	28.5	4	5	2	2
Trek Mult-Track 720	411	30	5	3	3	5
Univega Activa-ES	270	30.5	3	5	3	4

Brand and Model	On-Road Handling	Off-Road Handling	Shock Absrp.	Coasting	Seat Comfort	Gear Range Low/High	Frame Size
Bianchi Boardwalk	3	3	4	4	2	27/108	15.5-23
Cannondale SH400	3	3	1	3	3	25/104	19-25
Diamond Black	2	4	5	2	2	26/89	15.5-22
Giant Innova	4	2	3	2	2	24/96	15.5-23.5
Miyata Triple Cross	2	3	4	5	2	25/100	18-25
Nishiki Saga	3	2	1	5	1	24/96	16-22
Peugeot Limestone	3	3	3	5	5	27/108	18-24
Raleigh Eclipse CX	3	3	3	4	3	27/108	18-24
Ross Mt. Olympus XC	2	3	3	2	2	27/93	19.5-23
Schwinn Crisscross	2	4	4	3	3	27/100	18-22
Specialized Crossroads	3	3	4	3	3	25/100	16.5-22
Trek Mult-Track 720	3	3	3	4	2	25/100	17-23
Univega Activa-ES	2	3	3	3	4	27/93	16.6-22.5

Sports card collectors

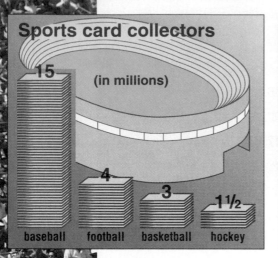

(in millions)

15 baseball
4 football
3 basketball
1½ hockey

Most popular sports

Number of people participating in each sport at least once in 1990 (in millions):

71.4	Exercise walking
67.5	Swimming
55.2	Bike riding
46.2	Camping
41.5	Freshwater fishing
40.1	Bowling
35.3	Exercising with equipment
26.3	Basketball
23.3	Aerobic exercising
23.2	Volleyball

AIDS epidemic

Number of cases reported annually

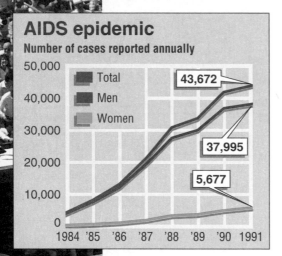

- Total
- Men
- Women

43,672
37,995
5,677

1984 '85 '86 '87 '88 '89 '90 1991

More green thumbs

Percentage of population involved in these lawn and plant activities:

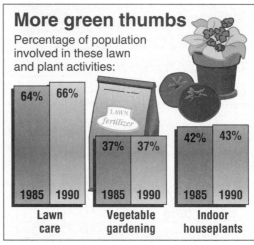

	Lawn care	Vegetable gardening	Indoor houseplants
1985	64%	37%	42%
1990	66%	37%	43%

Scouting rebounds

Number of boys and girls in Boy Scouts and Girl Scouts of America (in millions)

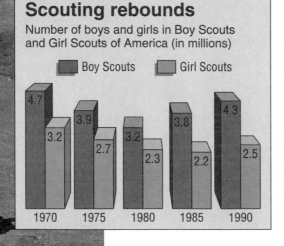

- Boy Scouts
- Girl Scouts

	1970	1975	1980	1985	1990
Boy Scouts	4.7	3.9	3.2	3.8	4.3
Girl Scouts	3.2	2.7	2.3	2.2	2.5

Cable TV explosion

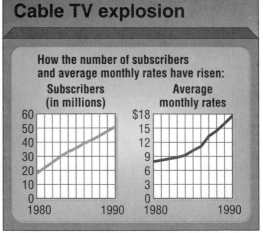

How the number of subscribers and average monthly rates have risen:

Subscribers (in millions)

60 50 40 30 20 10 0

1980 1990

Average monthly rates

$18 15 12 9 6 3 0

1980 1990

BASEBALL FORMULAS

$$AVG = \frac{H}{AB} \qquad ERA = \frac{9 \cdot ER}{IP}$$

$$SLG = \frac{TB}{AB} \qquad PCT = \frac{W}{W + L}$$

$$OB = \frac{H + BB}{AB + BB} \qquad WHIP = \frac{BB + H}{IP}$$

$$KIP = \frac{K}{IP}$$

$$TB = H + 2B + (2 \cdot 3B) + (3 \cdot HR)$$

Hitter's Key

G	games played
AB	times at bat
R	runs scored
H	hits
TB	total bases
2B	doubles
3B	triples
HR	homeruns
RBI	runs batted in
BB	walks (bases on balls)
SB	stolen bases
CS	caught stealing
SO	strikeouts
AVG	batting average
SLG	slugging percentage
OB	on-base percentage

Pitcher's Key

G	games played
IP	innings pitched
H	hits
W	wins
L	losses
R	runs
ER	earned runs
SO	strikeouts
BB	walks (bases on balls)
GS	games started
GF	games finished
CG	complete games
SHO	shut outs
SV	saves
ERA	earned run average
PCT	winning percentage
WHIP	walks-hits ratio
KIP	strikeout ratio

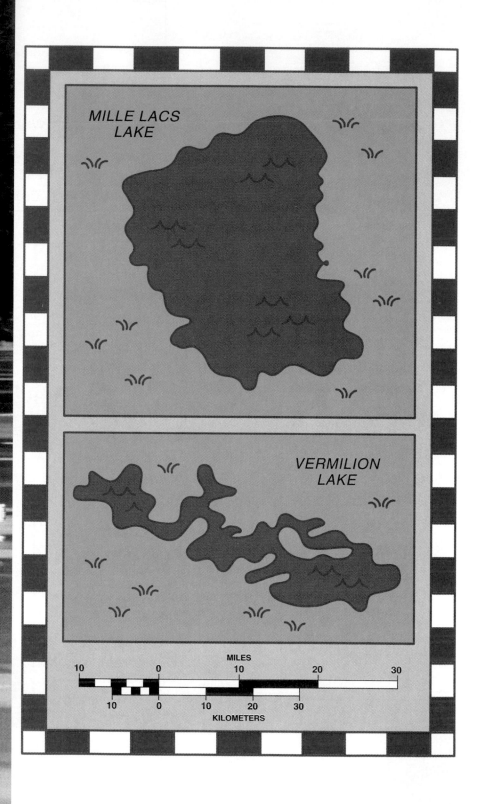

MILLE LACS
LAKE

VERMILION
LAKE

MILES

10   0   10   20   30

10   0   10   20   30

KILOMETERS

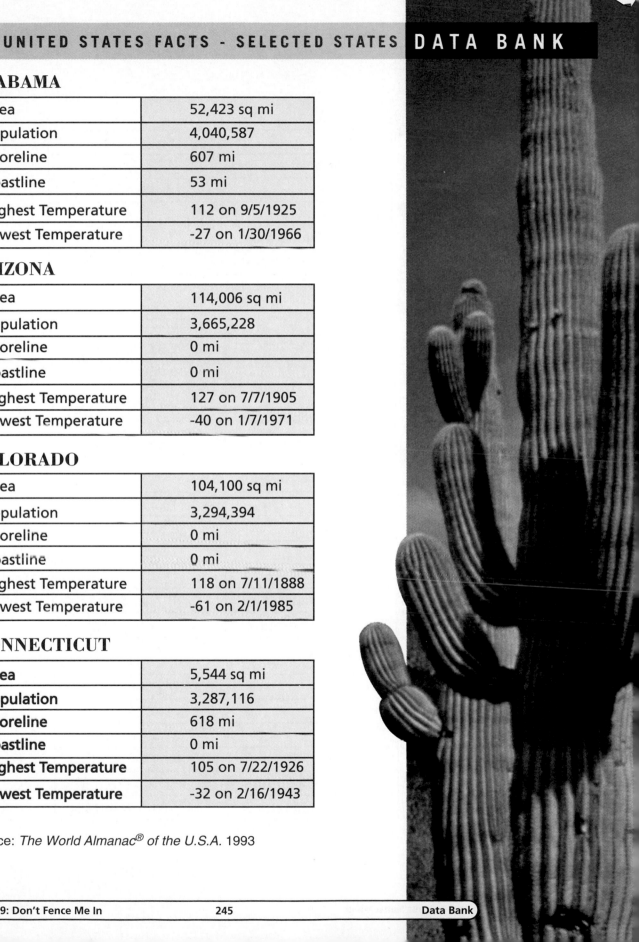

ALABAMA

Area	52,423 sq mi
Population	4,040,587
Shoreline	607 mi
Coastline	53 mi
Highest Temperature	112 on 9/5/1925
Lowest Temperature	-27 on 1/30/1966

ARIZONA

Area	114,006 sq mi
Population	3,665,228
Shoreline	0 mi
Coastline	0 mi
Highest Temperature	127 on 7/7/1905
Lowest Temperature	-40 on 1/7/1971

COLORADO

Area	104,100 sq mi
Population	3,294,394
Shoreline	0 mi
Coastline	0 mi
Highest Temperature	118 on 7/11/1888
Lowest Temperature	-61 on 2/1/1985

CONNECTICUT

Area	5,544 sq mi
Population	3,287,116
Shoreline	618 mi
Coastline	0 mi
Highest Temperature	105 on 7/22/1926
Lowest Temperature	-32 on 2/16/1943

Source: *The World Almanac® of the U.S.A.* 1993

FLORIDA

Area	65,758 sq mi
Population	12,937,926
Shoreline	8,426 mi
Coastline	1,350 mi
Highest Temperature	109 on 6/29/1931
Lowest Temperature	-2 on 2/13/1899

KANSAS

Area	82,282 sq mi
Population	2,477,574
Shoreline	0 mi
Coastline	0 mi
Highest Temperature	121 on 7/24/1936
Lowest Temperature	-40 on 2/13/1905

MASSACHUSETTS

Area	10,555 sq mi
Population	6,016,425
Shoreline	1,519 mi
Coastline	192 mi
Highest Temperature	107 on 8/2/1975
Lowest Temperature	-35 on 1/12/1981

MONTANA

Area	147,046 sq mi
Population	799,065
Shoreline	0 mi
Coastline	0 mi
Highest Temperature	117 on 7/5/1937
Lowest Temperature	-70 on 1/20/1954

Source: *The World Almanac® of the U.S.A.* 1993

NEW YORK

Area	54,475 sq mi
Population	17,990,455
Shoreline	1,850 mi
Coastline	127 mi
Highest Temperature	108 on 7/22/1926
Lowest Temperature	-52 on 2/18/1979

NORTH CAROLINA

Area	53,821 sq mi
Population	6,628,637
Shoreline	3,375 mi
Coastline	301 mi
Highest Temperature	110 on 8/21/1983
Lowest Temperature	-34 on 1/21/1985

TENNESSEE

Area	42,146 sq mi
Population	4,877,185
Shoreline	0 mi
Coastline	0 mi
Highest Temperature	113 on 8/9/1930
Lowest Temperature	-32 on 12/30/1917

UTAH

Area	84,904 sq mi
Population	1,722,850
Shoreline	0 mi
Coastline	0 mi
Highest Temperature	117 on 7/5/1985
Lowest Temperature	-69 on 2/1/1985

Source: *The World Almanac® of the U.S.A.* 1993

Game	Choose	From Digits	Number Correct	Payoff (on a $1 wager)
Pick 3 (straight)	3	0–9	3 in order	$500
Pick 3 (boxed)	3	0–9	3 in any order	3 different digits pays $83 3 digits with 2 the same pays $167
Pick 4 (straight)	4	0–9	4 in order	$5,000
Pick 4 (boxed)	4	0–9	4 in any order	4 different digits pays $200 4 digits with 2 the same pays $400 4 digits with 2 pairs the same pays $800 4 digits with 3 the same pays $1200
Buckeye 5	5	1–37	5	$100,000
Buckeye 5	5	1–37	4	$250
Buckeye 5	5	1–37	3	$10
Buckeye 5	5	1–37	2	$1
Super Lotto	6	1–47	6	varies, lowest jackpot is $4 million
Super Lotto	6	1–47	5	2.75% of sales
Super Lotto	6	1–47	4	8.59% of sales

Source: Ohio Lottery Commission

Note: If more than one person chooses 4, 5, or 6 numbers of the Super Lotto, the prize is divided equally among them. State law prohibits one winner from collecting more than $26 million on a Super Lotto prize.

The maximum payout for a Buckeye Five jackpot is $1 million. That means that up to ten people can win $100,000 for each drawing. If eleven winning tickets are sold for a drawing, each person would win $1,000,000 ÷ 11 or $90,909.

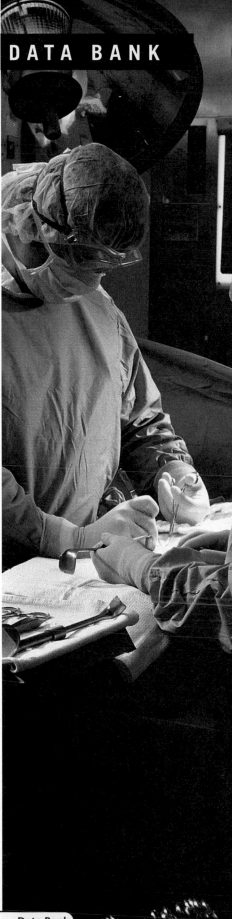

Cancer Death Rates by Site, U.S., 1930-1989

Females

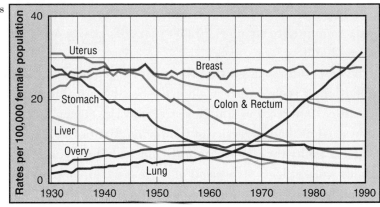

Rates per 100,000 female population

- Uterus
- Breast
- Stomach
- Colon & Rectum
- Liver
- Overy
- Lung

40 — 20 — 0

1930 1940 1950 1960 1970 1980 1990

Males

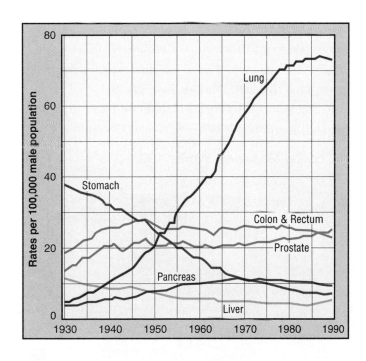

Rates per 100,000 male population

- Lung
- Stomach
- Colon & Rectum
- Prostate
- Pancreas
- Liver

80 — 60 — 40 — 20 — 0

1930 1940 1950 1960 1970 1980 1990

Source: American Cancer Society: rates adjusted to 1970 population

"Team of Scientists Contends Risk of California Quake is Overstated"

Government forecasts of disastrous earthquakes in California seriously exaggerate the risk, a team of scientists said today after using a computer to simulate 10,000 years of activity on the San Andreas Fault.

The new study suggests that the risk of a quake of 7.5 magnitude on the Richter scale or larger along the Southern California part of the fault is 19 percent within 30 years, said Dr. Steven Ward, a geophysicist at the University of California, Santa Cruz.

A forecast by the United States Geological Survey in 1988 said the odds were at least 60 percent in 30 years. The forecast was made and endorsed by panels representing a consensus of scientists. [Dr. Ward's] simulation suggested that big quakes happen almost randomly, rendering the government forecasts unreliable.

In little more than three years, three major quakes have hit California. The magnitude 7.1 Loma Prieta quake in 1989 killed 63 people in the San Francisco Bay region. The 7.1 Cape Medocino quake and its 6.7 and 6.6 aftershocks last April injured 356 people on the state's north coast. And on June 28, the 7.5 Landers quake and its 6.6 Big Bear aftershock killed a child and injured 402 Southern Californians. (*New York Times*, December 9, 1992)

Source: *Chance Magazine,* Winter 1993, p. 6

Home and Away Records for Major League Baseball Division Winners, 1969–1989		
	Number of Games	**Win Percentage**
Home	6,670	63.3
Away	6,680	55.3
All Games	13,350	59.3

Source: *Chance Magazine,* Spring 1993, p. 32

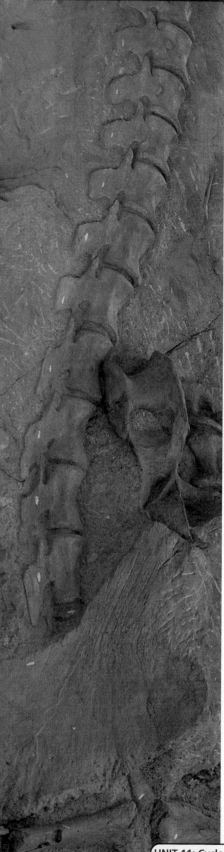

InGen Corporation

Lab Report

Fossil: FQ26754

Location of Find: La Chapelle-aux Saints, France

Test performed:

Carbon-14 Dating

Bone-Structure Analysis

Date test performed: Jan. 15, 1993

Time test performed: 12:00 noon

Carbon-Dating Results: 43,457.625 years

Bone-Structure Analysis Results: 24.25 years

Notes:

<u>Carbon-14 dating</u> determines the actual time a fossil (bone) has existed, starting from the time the creature died.

<u>Bone structure analysis</u> is a process in which a fossil is analyzed to determine the development of the bone, thus providing the approximate age of the once-living creature at the time of death.

Tests performed by: Dr. Bette Wright Knott

Time Conversions

1,000 nanoseconds = 1 second

100 milliseconds = 1 second

60 seconds = 1 minute

60 minutes = 1 hour

3,600 seconds = 1 hour

24 hours = 1 day

7 days = 1 week

365 days = 1 year

366 days = 1 leap year

52 weeks + 1 day = 1 year

12 months = 1 year

3 months = 1 season

4 seasons = 1 year

10 years = 1 decade

2 decades = 1 score

100 years = 1 century

Seasons

Winter is from December 21 to March 21.

Spring is from March 22 to June 20.

Summer is from June 21 to September 20.

Autumn is from September 21 to December 20.

Days in the Month

January has 31 days.

February has 28 or 29 days.

March has 31 days.

April has 30 days.

May has 31 days.

June has 30 days.

July has 31 days.

August has 31 days.

September has 30 days.

October has 31 days.

November has 30 days.

December has 31 days.

Leap Year occurs every four years on years divisible by 4. For example, 1992 was a leap year because 1992 divided by 4 has no remainder. The one exception occurs every odd turn of the century in years such as 1500, 1700, 1900, and so on. These are not leap years.

Type	Leap Year	January 1	December 31
1	No	Sunday	Sunday
2	No	Monday	Monday
3	No	Tuesday	Tuesday
4	No	Wednesday	Wednesday
5	No	Thursday	Thursday
6	No	Friday	Friday
7	No	Saturday	Saturday
8	Yes	Sunday	Monday
9	Yes	Monday	Tuesday
10	Yes	Tuesday	Wednesday
11	Yes	Wednesday	Thursday
12	Yes	Thursday	Friday
13	Yes	Friday	Saturday
14	Yes	Saturday	Sunday

Calendars: 1899–2040

Year...Type	Year...Type	Year...Type	Year...Type	Year...Type	Year...Type
1899...1	1901...3	1929...3	1957...3	1985...3	2013...3
1900...2	1902...4	1930...4	1958...4	1986...4	2014...4
	1903...5	1931...5	1959...5	1987...5	2015...5
	1904...13	1932...13	1960...13	1988...13	2016...13
	1905...1	1933...1	1961...1	1989...1	2017...1
	1906...2	1934...2	1962...2	1990...2	2018...2
	1907...3	1935...3	1963...3	1991...3	2019...3
	1908...11	1936...11	1964...11	1992...11	2020...11
	1909...6	1937...6	1965...6	1993...6	2021...6
	1910...7	1938...7	1966...7	1994...7	2022...7
	1911...1	1939...1	1967...1	1995...1	2023...1
	1912...9	1940...9	1968...9	1996...9	2024...9
	1913...4	1941...4	1969...4	1997...4	2025...4
	1914...5	1942...5	1970...5	1998...5	2026...5
	1915...6	1943...6	1971...6	1999...6	2027...6
	1916...14	1944...14	1972...14	2000...14	2028...14
	1917...2	1945...2	1973...2	2001...2	2029...2
	1918...3	1946...3	1974...3	2002...3	2030...3
	1919...4	1947...4	1975...4	2003...4	2031...4
	1920...12	1948...12	1976...12	2004...12	2032...12
	1921...7	1949...7	1977...7	2005...7	2033...7
	1922...1	1950...1	1978...1	2006...1	2034...1
	1923...2	1951...2	1979...2	2007...2	2035...2
	1924...10	1952...10	1980...10	2008...10	2036...10
	1925...5	1953...5	1981...5	2009...5	2037...5
	1926...6	1954...6	1982...6	2010...6	2038...6
	1927...7	1955...7	1983...7	2011...7	2039...7
	1928...8	1956...8	1984...8	2012...8	2040...8

DATA BANK HUMAN PROPORTIONS

Leonardo da Vinci was an artist who lived from 1452 to 1519. Through his study of human anatomy, da Vinci discovered some interesting proportions in the human body. He drew a figure similar to the one at the right to illustrate his findings. He wrote, "If you set your legs so far apart as to take a fourteenth part from your height, and you open and raise your arms until you touch the line of the crown of your head with your middle fingers,... the center of the circle formed by the ... limbs will be the navel, and the space between the legs will form an equilateral triangle." The circle around the figure illustrates this.

The measures of the ancient Egyptians were based on the proportions of the human body. The Egyptians used parts of the body as measuring tools. Some of the units are shown below.

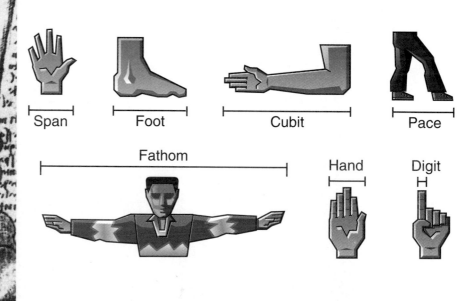

Span   Foot   Cubit   Pace

Fathom   Hand   Digit

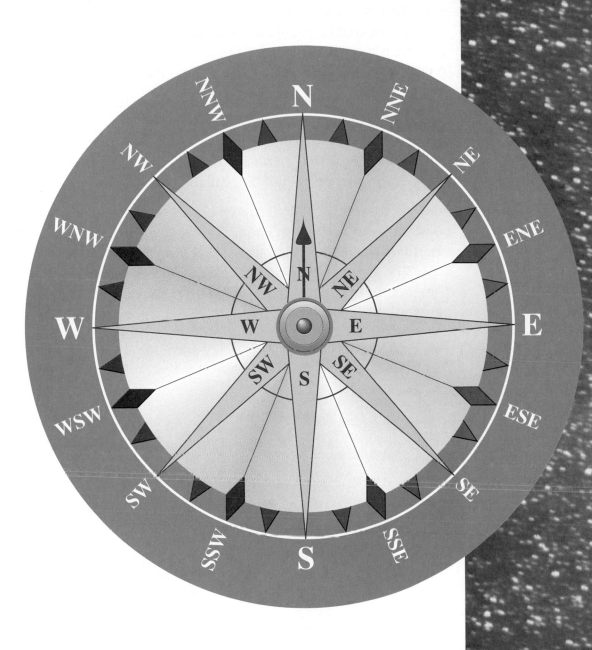

A grid made up of north-south and east-west lines is used on maps for finding and describing locations on the Earth's surface. The grid lines are called *meridians* and *parallels*. Each grid line is a circle or part of a circle. The grid lines are shown in degrees because circles may be divided into degrees.

Meridians are north-south lines drawn from pole to pole through the equator. Each meridian is a half-circle. The meridian that runs through Greenwich, England is labeled 0° and is called the *prime meridian.* The distance in degrees of any location east or west of 0° is called its **longitude.**

Parallels are east-west lines drawn around a globe so that all points on each line are an equal distance from a pole. The *equator* is the parallel that is an equal distance from both poles. The equator is labeled 0° and each pole is labeled 90°. The distance in degrees of any location north or south of the equator is called its **latitude.**

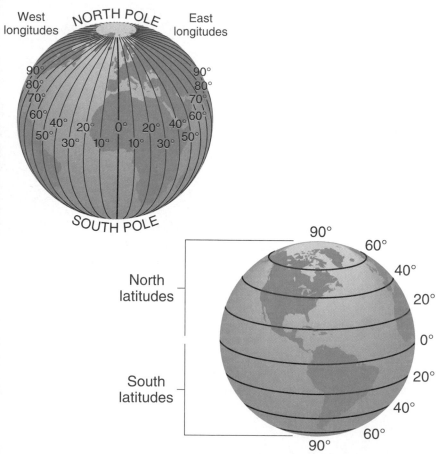

The island you seek is part of a group of islands seen by Columbus on his last voyage to America. Because they were inhabited by thousands of turtles, he named them Las Tortugas. Later the Spanish renamed them for the Spanish word for alligator. However, since there are no alligators on the islands, the Spanish may have been describing large iguanas or crocodiles that are seen in the area.

During the 1700s, very real pirates operated from bases on these low-lying islands. Blackbeard hid his treasure in caves on the islands. Sir Henry Morgan, the British privateer, established his base on the main island. Morgan was famous for the sacking of Porto Bello. He amassed prizes estimated at over $3 million. Later he served as British Governor of Jamaica.

Today there are almost as many banks and companies as people on the islands. Financial activity has become the mainstay of the islands' economy. There are no taxes and there are strict bank confidentiality laws.

The islands are surrounded by some of the finest diving areas in the world. Underwater visibility is excellent. Divers come to explore the coral reefs and numerous shipwrecks.

The national symbol is a turtle dressed as a pirate.

What is this island?

Letters and Percent of Their Usage in Ordinary Text Material

A - 8.2	B - 1.4	C - 2.8	D - 3.8
E - 13.0	F - 3.0	G - 2.0	H - 5.3
I - 6.5	J - 0.1	K - 0.4	L - 3.4
M - 2.5	N - 7.0	O - 8.0	P - 2.0
Q - 0.1	R - 6.8	S - 6.0	T - 10.5
U - 2.5	V - 0.9	W - 1.5	X - 0.2
Y - 2.0	Z - 0.07		

Source: NCTM: Student Math Notes, January 1983

GLOSSARY INDEX

A

Accuracy, 130, 141

Acres, 104

Actual outcomes, 137

Acute angles, 203

Addition, 160, 161, 179

Address, 94 consists of a letter and a numeral to indicate the respective column and row in which the cell in a spreadsheet is located

Adds, 122

Algebra
coordinate plane, 78
negative sign, 160, 173
ordered pairs, 78, 79, 89, 157
point, 78, 79, 80, 89
positive sign, 160, 173
scale, 78
timeline, 157
variables, 116
x-axis, 78
y-axis, 78

Align, 99

Analysis, 167, 173, 176, 252

Analyze, 44, 64, 146
data, 63

Angle, 9, 11, 197, 215, 219, 220, 221, 222-223, 225
formed when two segments of a polygon meet
acute, 203
bisect, 197, 219, 222
construct, 197, 222
exterior, 215, 216
interior, 225
measurement of, 200, 203, 207, 210, 214, 215, 219, 223, 225, 226
opposite, 12
right, 11, 99, 203, 207, 223
straight, 203
string, 219

Approximate, 72, 237

Arc, 219, 220

Area, 13, 20, 30, 73, 74, 75, **76,** 77, 83, 84, 85, 86, 87, 88, 90, 91, 92, 93, 94, 95, 96, 97, 98, 99, 100, 101, 102, 103, 105, 106, 107, 111, 112, 113, 218, 245, 246, 247
the number of square units needed to cover a surface
circle, 111
parallelograms, 73, 99
rectangular, 84, 93, 97
triangles, 73, 97, 98

Arithmetic, 179

Average, 31, 36, 39, 41, 42, 49, 51, 52, 53, 54, 55, 66, 67, 70, 120, 160, 242
distance, 229
income, 161
monthly rates, 242
number, 173

B

Balance, 161

Bar graph, 33, 56, 59

Base, 99, 103, 111, 188

Base of a parallelogram, 99 one of the sides of a parallelogram

Base of a triangle, 98 any one of the sides of a triangle

Base-ten, 155, 196

Bases of a trapezoid, 13 the parallel sides of a trapezoid

Basic program, 142

Bisect angles, 197, 219, 222

Boot, 142

Brakes, 240, 241

Budget, 45, 159

C

Calculate, 86, 87, 92, 94, 156, 187, 188, 225

Calculated, 120

Calculation, 116

Calculators, 1, 2, 39, 41, 78, 120, 159, 160, 161

Cells, 94 a large arrangement of boxes created by a spreadsheet program, each of which has its own address

Celsius, 187

Center, 131, 207, 256

Centimeter, 20
grid paper, 8, 20, 85, 88, 91, 95, 96, 99, 101, 111

Centimeters, 91, 229

Cents, 74

Centuries, 170, 196, 253, 254

Certain, 103 an event having a probability of one

Chances, 21, 103, 104, 118, 119, 120, 129, 142, 145, 153

Charts, 7, 36, 43, 71, 111, 146

Circles, 18, 20, 29, 111, 131, 174, 176, 191, 195, 203, 212

Circular pattern, 203

Circumference, 20, 111

Coasting, 240

Column, 22, 94, 98, 133, 161, 240

Combination, 153, 154, 195

Commands, 157, 215
LOGO, 216

Compare, 97, 101

Compass, 130, 131, 140, 197, 219, 220, 221, 222, 223

GLOSSARY INDEX

Figure, 96, 99, 105, 215, 216, 223
  geometric, 197, 234

Forecast, 250

Formulas, 13, 92, 94, 243

Fraction, 101, 103, 129, 131

Frequency, 217

Frequency table, 33, **39,** 40 a chart that indicates the number of values in each interval

G

Gear range, 240

Geoband, 97, 98

Geometric
  figures, 197, 234
  shapes, 73

Geometry, 4, 156
  angle, **9,** 197, 200, 203, 207, 214, 220, 222-223, 225
  arc, 219, 220
  area, 13, 20, 73, 74, 75, **76,** 77, 83, 84, 85, 86, 87, 88, 90, 91, 92, 93, 94, 95, 96, 97, 98, 99, 100, 101, 102, 103, 105, 106, 107, 111, 112, 113, 218, 245, 246, 247
  base, 13, **99,** 103, 111
  center, 131, 156, 207, 256
  circles, 18, 20, 29, 111, 131, 174, 176, 191, 195, 203, 212
  circumference, 20, 111
  compass, 130, 131, 140, 197, 219, 220, 221, 222, 223
  congruent, **9,** 11, 12
  cubes, 28
  cylinder, 20
  diameter, 229
  distance, 4, 13, 116, 197, 212, 215, 219, 220
  endpoint, 220
  equilateral triangle, 221,

222, 233
  face, 28
  height, **13,** 20, 97, 98, 99
  isosceles triangles, **11, 223**
  length, 20, 30, 77, 78, 86, 93, 94, 99, 101, 102, 116
  line, 80, 99, 123, 124, 125, 126, 127, 134, 135, 136, 207
  line segment, 9
  parallel, 13
  parallelogram, 4, **9,** 12, 73, 99
  perimeter, 73, 75, 76, 80, 84, 86, 88, 89, 92, 101, 105, 106, 107, 110
  point, 78, 79, 80, 89, 131, 150, 207, 208, 215, 219, 220
  polygon, 9, 214, 226
  protractor, 130, 131, 140, 197, 203, **204,** 207, 214, 221, 224
  quadrilateral, 4, **9**
  radius, 111, 131
  ray, 220
  rectangle, 4, 10, 20, 32, 73, 77, 84, 86, 91, 93, 97, 99, 102, 103, 114, 214, 215
  rhombus, 4
  right angle, 194
  rotation, 207
  sides, 84, 92, 97, 101, 102, 216, 219, 220, 221, 223, 225
  square, 4, 8, **9,** 10, 11, 12, 18, 26, 30, 91, 97, 101, 102, 111, 131, 150, 203, 215
  trapezoid, 4, **13**
  triangle, **9,** 11, 12, 17, 29, 73, 97, 99, 103, 214, 221, 223, 233
  vertex, **9, 207,** 219, 220
  vertical line, 131
  vertices, 8

Gigabytes, 178

Graph paper, 214

Graphs, 21, 33, 35, 45, 57, 59, 60, 62, 143, 146
  bar graph, 33, 56, 68, 69
  histogram, 40, 43, 57, 58, 61, 64
  line, 78, 90
  line plot, 42, 48
  pictograph, 68
  stem-and-leaf plot, 38, 39

Greatest number, 173

Grid, 32, 99, **258** made up of north-south and east-west lines and used on maps for finding and describing locations
  paper, 92, 106

Grid lines, 258 meridians and parallels shown in degrees

Group, 38, 39

H

Handling, 240

Height, 20, 39, 97, 98, 99, 209, 256

Height of a parallelogram, 99 the distance from the base of a parallelogram to the opposite side

Height of a trapezoid, 13 the shortest distance between its bases

Height of a triangle, 97 the distance from the base of a triangle to the opposite vertex

Hexagon, 14 a polygon having six sides

Hexagonal numbers, 234

V

Values, 38

Variables, 116

Vertex, 9, 207, 219, 220   the point where two segments of a polygon meet; the point where angles meet

Vertical line, 131

Vertices, 8, 14

Volume, 187

W

Week, 77, 79, 80, 118

Weight, 37, 38, 39, 40, 41, 116, 187, 240, 241

Whole number, 173

Width, 20, 77, 86, 93, 94

X

X-axis, 78

Y

Y-axis, 78

Yards, 113, 187

Year, 34, 56, 59, 74, 75, 116, 157, 159, 161, 168, 169, 170, 171, 172, 178, 186, **187**, 190, 196, 237, 250, 252, 253, 254, 255   one rotation of earth around the sun

PHOTO CREDITS

COVER: (background), Scott Morgan/Westlight, (t), Jack Holtel, (cl), Co Rentmeester, (cr), Ken Straiton/The Stock Market, (bl), Lou Jones/The Image Bank; (br), Todd Yarrington

iii (l), BLT Productions/Brent Turner, (r), Life Images; ix, Courtsey Melody Daughters; x, xi, Courtesy Catco, Inc/Mary Rodas; xiii, Kim Williams; xiv, BLT Productions/Brent Turner; xv Tom Treick; xvi, Giuseppe Ferrara; xvii, Courtesy Laruie Moran; xviii, Mike Yamashita/Westlight; 1(l), Courtesy Melody Daughters, (r), Crown Studios; 2(t), Courtesy Melody Daughters, (l), 3(r), Crown Studios, (screened), K S Studios/Bob Mullenix, (cl), The Bettmann Archive, (cr), Courtesy Melody Daughters, (bl), Courtesy The Seeing Eye, Morristown, NJ; 5, Life Images; 7, Elaine Comer-Shay; 8, Mak-1; 9, Life Images; 10, K S Studios/Bob Mullenix; 11, Wayne Eastep/The Stock Market; 12(l), Lee Yunker, (r), Mak-1; 13, Bob Rowan/AllStock; 14, Life Images; 15, Charlie Benes/Photobank; 16, Elaine Comer-Shay; 17, Ohio Department of Natural Resources; 18, Spencer Grant/Photobank; 19, Bob Daemmrich/Stock Boston; 20, K S Studios/Bob Mullenix; 21, Jim Corwin/AllStock; 22(l), Animals Animals, (r), J. M. Labat/Photo Researchers; 23, Studiohio; 24, Rick Weber; 25, Jurgens/Europa-Photo; 26(l), Life Images, (r), Billy E. Barnes/Stock Boston; 27, Studiohio; 28, Elaine Comer-Shay; 29,30, Rick Weber; 31, Ken Frick; 32, Mark Gibson; 33, 34, Courtesy Catco,Inc/Mary Rodas; 35(t), BLT Productions/Brent Turner, (cl), Latent Image, (all others), Courtesy Catco, Inc/Mary Rodas; 36, BLT Productions/Brent Turner; 37, Aaron Haupt; 39, BLT Productions/Brent Turner; 42(t), Tim Davis/Photo Researchers, (c), Jeffrey Sylvester/FPG,(b), BLT Productions/Brent Turner; 43(tl), Jonathan Selig/Photo 20-20, (tr), Ed Lettau/FPG, (bl), C. Hamilton/PhotoBank, (r), Aaron Haupt; 44, Doug Martin; 45, Tim Courlas; 47, BLT Productions/Brent Turner; 49, Life Images; 50, Doug Martin; 51, Life Images; 52(l), Ira Block/The Image Bank, (r), Doug Martin; 53, Greg Ryan, Sally Beyer/Allstock; 54, David Barnes/Allstock; 55(l), Todd Yarrington, (r), Aaron Haupt; 56, Mitchell B. Raibel/Sports Photo Masters; 57, Robert Chapek/PhotoBank; 58, Alain Choisnet/The Image Bank; 59, 60, Aaron Haupt; 61(l), Courtesy of The Coca-Cola Company, (tr), F. Stuart Westmorland/Allstock, (br), Lawrence Migdale; 62, Joseph Szkodzinski/The Image Bank; 63, Dennis Hallinan; 64, 65, BLT Productions/Brent Turner; 66, Jeff Bates Photography; 67, Jonathan Kirn/Sports Photo Masters; 68(t), NBC/Shooting Star, (c), Steve Jennings/LGI Photo Agency, (b), Dean Dixon/LGI Photo Agency; 69, Jeff Bates Photography; 70, 71, Aaron Haupt Photography; 72, Doug Martin; 73(l), Kim Williams, (r), Susan Rhoades-Martin; 74(t), Kim Williams, (l), Susan Rhoades-Martin; 75(t), Scott Cunningham, (r), Susan Rhoades-Martin; (screened), Matt Meadows, (cl), Mary Evans Picture Library, (bl), Culver Pictures, Inc, (bc), Kim Williams; 76-77(b), Matt Meadows, 76-77(all others),79, 80, Scott Cunningham; 82, Annie Griffiths/West Light; 83, Rick Weber; 84, Bob Daemmrich Photography; 85, Rick Weber; 86, Matt Meadows; 87, Mercury Archives/The Image Bank; 89, The Image Bank; 90(l), file photo; (r), Craig Kramer; 91, Rick Weber; 92, Dennis MacDonald/PhotoEdit; 93, Jane T. Sepinsky/The Stock Market; 95, Matt Meadows; 96, 97, Rick Weber; 98, David Barnes/AllStock; 99, Rick Weber; 100, Mark E. Gibson; 101, Tony Freeman/PhotoEdit; 103, Matt Meadows; 104, Rick Weber; 105(l), Matt Meadows; (r), David Doody/FPG; 106, Michael Collier; 107, file photo;

108, Matt Meadows; 109, Tom McCarthy/PhotoEdit; 110, 111, Rick Weber; 112, Matt Meadows; 113, Fukuhara, Inc./West Light; 114, Bob Daemmrich Photography; 115(l), Tom Treick, (r), 116(l), Richard Hamilton Smith/AllStock, (t), Tom Treick; 117(t), BLT Productions/Brent Turner, (r), Richard Hamilton Smith/AllStock, (screened), Aaron Haupt Photography, (cl), Bill Ross/AllStock, (cr), Tom Treick, (bl), Culver Pictures, Inc, (br), Art Wolfe/AllStock; 118(b), Richard Pasley/Stock Boston, (all others), BLT Productions/Brent Turner; 120, 121, BLT Productions/Brent Turner, 122, Bill Ross/Westlight; 123(t), Matt Meadows, (b), Aaron Haupt Photography; 124, Ross Hickson; 125(l), BLT Productions/Brent Turner, (r), K S Studios/Bob Mullenix; 126, 127, BLT Productions/Brent Turner; 128(l), Bob Daemmrich/Stock Boston, (r), Aaron Haupt Photography; 129(l), Brownie Harris/The Stock Market, (r), David Barnes/AllStock; 130(l), Mark E. Gibson, (r), Aaron Haupt Photography; 132, Matt Meadows; 133, Rafael Macia/Photo Researchers; 135, K S Studios/Bob Mullenix; 136, Aaron Haupt Photography; 137, Todd Yarrington; 138, Rick Weber; 139, Life Images; 140, Doug Martin; 141, 142, Life Images; 143, BLT Productions/Brent Turner; 144, Life Images; 145, Don Smith/Sports Photo Masters; 146, Robert W. Ginn/PhotoEdit; 147(tl), Rick Weber, (tc), Gay Bumgarner/AllStock, (bl), Michael Furman/The Stock Market, (bc), David C. Bitters/Photo Resources, (r), Bachmann/Photo Researchers; 148(l), Life Images, (r), K S Studios/Bob Mullenix; 149, Elaine Comer-Shay; 150(l), David Woods/The Stock Market, (r), Frank Oberle/Photo Resources; 151, K S Studios/Bob Mullenix; 152(t), Michael Grecco/Stock Boston, (b), Life Images; 153, David Young-Wolff/PhotoEdit; 154(l), Lois Ellen Frank/Westlight, (r), Life Images; 155(l), Giuseppe Ferrara, (r), K S Studios/Bob Mullenix; 156(t), Giuseppe Ferrara, (l), K S Studios/Bob Mullenix; 157(t), BLT Productions/Brent Turner, (r), K S Studios/Bob Mullenix, (screened), Giuseppe Ferrara, (cl), Ken Straighton/The Stock Market, (cc), William W. Bacon,III/AllStock, (cr), The Bettmann Archive, (b), The Singer Sewing Company, Edison, NJ; 158, 159, Scott Cunningham; 160(t), Renee Lynn/Photo Researchers, (b), Scott Cunningham; 161, Aaron Haupt Photography; 162, 163, Scott Cunningham; 164, Larry Hamill; 165, 166, Scott Cunningham; 167(l), K S Studios/Bob Mullenix, (r), Paul Brown; 168, James W. Kay/PhotoBank; 169, Masa Uemura/AllStock; 170(l)(tr), Scott Cunningham, (br), Aaron Haupt Photography; 171(l), H. Armstrong Roberts, (r), George Oremski/The Image Bank; 172(l), Gerard Photography, (r), Life Images; 173, Focus On Sports; 174, K S Studios/Bob Mullenix; 175, Scott Cunningham; 176, S. Hellerstein/The Stock Market; 177, Everett Collection; 178(l), K S Studios/Bob Mullenix, (r), Ron Kimball Studios; 179, Marvin E. Newman/The Image Bank; 180, Doug Martin; 181, Steve Dunwell/The Image Bank; 182, Stephen J. Krasemann/Photo Researchers; 183, Animals Animals/Patti Murray; 184, Aaron Haupt Photography; 185(l), Courtesy Tiara Observatory/Tersch, (r), Jim Corwin/Photo Researchers; 186, Tim Courlas; 187, 188, NASA; 189, E. R. Degginger; 190(l), Aaron Haupt Photography, (r), Scott Cunningham; 191(l), Life Images, (r), Mak-1; 192, Scott Cunningham; 193(t), Aaron Haupt Photography, (b), Mak-1; 194, 195, Life Images; 196, Tom Carroll/FPG; 197(l), Courtesy Laurie Moran, (r), 198(l), David Doody/FPG, (t), Courtesy Laurie Moran; 199(t), Scott Cunningham, (r), David Doody/FPG, (screened), Index Stock Photogrpahy, (c), The Bettmann Archive; (bl), Spencer Jones/FPG, (bc), Index Stock